Born Together

Born Together

Patricia Gachagan

Matador
9 Priory Business Park,
Wistow Road, Kibworth Beauchamp,
Leicestershire. LE8 0RX
Tel: 0116 279 2299
Email: books@troubador.co.uk
Web: www.troubador.co.uk/matador
Twitter: @matadorbooks

ISBN 978 1788036 979

British Library Cataloguing in Publication Data.
A catalogue record for this book is available from the British Library.

Printed and bound in the UK by TJ International, Padstow, Cornwall
Typeset in 11pt Adobe Garamond Pro by Troubador Publishing Ltd, Leicester, UK

Matador is an imprint of Troubador Publishing Ltd

This book is dedicated to my wonderful son, Elliot and my amazing husband, Allan. They have shared every step of this journey with positivity, love and determination.

'She stood in the storm, and when the wind did not blow her way – and it surely has not – she adjusted her sails.'
                                                    (Elizabeth Edwards)

Contents

Foreword by Judy Graham   xi
Acknowledgements   xiii
Preface   xv
Thank You   xix
About Multiple Sclerosis   xxi
In the Beginning   xxv

1. The Birth   1
2. Getting Worse   7
3. The Apartment   17
4. A Busy Summer   22
5. An Even Busier Autumn   31
6. 'A Winter of Discontent'   42
7. The News   49
8. My Brush with Neurology   61
9. Onwards and Upwards   71
10. Reaching Out   90
11. Early Retirement   97
12. Dr Gilhooly   101
13. Complementary Care   108
14. Elliot Starts Nursery   113
15. CCSVI Procedure (Chronic Cerebrospinal
    Venous Insufficiency)   117
16. Post-CCSVI   132

17. Elliot Starts School   138
18. Disbelief   146
19. wecanfindaway.com   153
20. Cold Feet and Lead Legs   164
21. Goodbye to Shoe Heaven   168
22. Motherhood   173
23. Acceptance   182
24. My Wife has MS   188
25. My Mum has MS   196
26. Travelling   202
27. Discrimination   212
28. The Fall   220
29. Getting Back Up   230
30. Another Setback   237
31. Hope Returns   241
32. Earthing   247
33. Counselling   252
34. Writing   257
35. Chongsu Lee   263
36. My Own Little Miracle   270
37. Robo-Physio   277
38. What's Next?   283

References   294

Foreword

Judy Graham, author

Patricia Gachagan has written a totally inspirational book about having MS. Her motto is you can find a way, no matter what the adversity. The trick is to accept and adapt, to live every moment of every day to the utmost; to see everything in your life as more precious than it was before. When MS knocked her for six after the birth of her beloved son Elliot, Patricia could have lost hope and spiralled downwards. Instead, she was able to alter the way she looked at her situation and change negatives into positives. She battled on, striding up steep hills both physical and metaphorical to be the best mother possible to her son, always at her side with a helping hand. She started searching for the pieces of the jigsaw puzzle that would set her on the road to being well. She rejected the 'cold and lonely' medical route and said no to disease-modifying drugs from her neurologist. She scorned those who labelled her a pitiful victim and didn't have the time of day for people who predicted worsening disability. She rejected rejection, refused to feel inferior or ashamed because she had MS. Instead of disabled, Patricia sees herself as 'differently abled', something to be celebrated rather than denigrated. It's an uplifting philosophy that can change your life, so it's worth getting your head around it. The start of each chapter has an inspirational quote to help you see things in a different and more positive light.

Born Together shows Patricia's indomitable spirit in her quest for finding a way to a full, happy and healthy life. I feel privileged for having played a part in this. The fascinating journey told in this book describes the changes she made to her diet, the nutritional supplements she takes, the importance of exercise, the need to be mindful and reduce stress, and the benefits of Earthing. The last piece of the jigsaw is the 'miracle' physiotherapy given by Korean Chongsu Lee in Edinburgh, which made a dramatic difference to her walking and well-being. Patricia is truly the heroine of her own life. This wonderfully uplifting book might help you be the same.

Judy Graham

Acknowledgements

'Alone we can do so little; together we can do so much.'
(Helen Keller)

Writing *Born Together* has been part of a wonderful journey. Many wonderful people have helped me on that journey:

Allan Johnston; grammar check, IT manager, printer, problem-solver!

Elliot Gachagan; thesaurus, writing enthusiast, inspiration guru, creative director!

Margaret Anne Gachagan; book reviewer, listener, social media adviser, admin manager, sounding-board!

Margaret Gachagan; absolute all-rounder!

Liz Ellis; book reviewer, positivity guru!

Elizabeth Thompson; book reviewer, morale booster!

Lorna Evans; book reviewer, pro-active supporter!

Elaine Collins; book reviewer, life enthusiast!

Helen McNally; book reviewer, enthusiastic supporter!

Steven Griffiths; web designer, problem-solver, nothing's-a-bother person!

Caitlin Miller; book cover artist

Dawn McManus; inside cover graphic artist

Lorraine Hudson; inside cover artist

All the support and contributions made *Born Together* possible. I am very grateful and offer huge thanks and love to everyone involved.

Preface

'You must do the things you think you cannot do.'
(Eleanor Roosevelt)

I have always believed I would write a book since I was in my early twenties. It was something I kept at a distance and toyed with from time to time. It was evermore about finding the right subject matter and a time in my life that would allow me to write. I would never in my wildest dreams have thought it would have been written about having Multiple Sclerosis and at a time where I could no longer work due to my physical health. I did have a short-lived six-week marriage when I was twenty-five. That offered some writing material, but not much more than a short story and a comedic one at that!

When I was teaching at a school in North London, a truly inspirational boy in my year six class, called Joss, asked me as I was scribbling some notes, 'What are you doing Miss?' I told him I was writing and he continued by asking me, 'What about Miss?' I said that I was writing about myself. He replied, 'You must find yourself really interesting Miss.' Those words have always stayed with me. I have known since then writing a book had to be about something that would really tell a story, something that would offer hope and unlimited inspiration. I also knew the book would come and find me. It has and it is a story of my journey through change and acceptance, a journey where nothing and no one stayed the same. My book shares how motherhood and Multiple Sclerosis were 'born together'. An exceptional experience, but one that has galvanised me to embrace all that life throws at you and to live every moment of every day without any hesitation. I have found good times in the darkest of moments and my love is overwhelming for my family and my life.

This book takes you through my self-help voyage, which commenced on the very day of my diagnosis. There has never been a day since where I have not been on it. I have tried and tested just about everything there is out there in relation to improving my quality of life with Multiple Sclerosis. Some have proved better than others. I have tried to find fun in just about everything. I have laughed more than I have cried. When I have cried, I have tried to change the thing that made me cry. When I have laughed, I've made certain to do it again.

I have learned to see whatever I've got as much more precious and valuable than I ever did before. My whole thought process has been realigned. I have always tried to be a positive person, but now I have no room for complaint or negativity in my life. I need to grasp everything I possibly can and make the best of the cards I have been dealt. That is at best challenging and very often difficult. But I have learned that it can be done and with a smile too. If we just change our perspective a little, then we can change a lot. Everyone has their own battle going on in life. I have mine. We often cannot change what those battles are, but we can change how we approach and deal with them. We can let them knock us over and feel the pain life throws at us. That can be overwhelming at times. We can also fight back with everything we have got. We can choose to see the positives hidden in each thing. We can take strength from those and from the things we have got. I have chosen to do all of that.

That was inevitably going to be my decision. It is not always straightforward, but it is a way forward. We use a phrase in our house all the time, 'wecanfindaway.com'. This was coined in the early days as we tried to find different ways to do many ordinary things, particularly when Elliot was a newborn baby. This phrase is now part of our everyday language and so too is the fact we always do find a way! We can all reach inside and find the capacity to shift our outlook on life. We can learn to appreciate what we have got and be more content with less. No one knows what is around the corner. But we do know who we are and what we have today. If it's not good, we can do everything we can to change the direction we are going in. Never stop trying. There is so much we can achieve depending on our attitude.

Born Together explores all I did to steer what seemed to be my destiny in a different direction. The work never stops. The rewards are immense for all my efforts. I was knocked down by my diagnosis, but I got straight back up again. I always will. Others can too.

Thank You

'As we express our gratitude, we must never forget that the highest appreciation is not to utter words, but to live by them.'

(JF Kennedy)

I thank my husband Allan and my son Elliot for being the best friends you could have. I thank them for supporting the very tired and jaded wife and mum after I had spent the day writing. I thank them too for their understanding and absolute acceptance that home life became different for quite some time while I was writing. The notes, the papers, the books, the piles laid around never to be touched! And they never were. They sat side by side with Elliot's toys. I thank Allan for being my grammar check and Elliot for being my thesaurus! I could not have done it without them.

At times we had to dig in deep, but Allan is the master of resilience and has been a great teacher and support for both me and Elliot. We have learned well from him. Thank you for never running out of time, patience, strength and fight. Thank you Elliot, for giving me all and more than you could ask for in one lifetime. You are inspirational and I watch this space with great excitement and faith in whatever you choose to do.

I thank my sister and great friend Margaret Anne, for

saying yes every time I asked her to do anything. And I asked a lot. To my mum also for always being there, never faltering even in the toughest of times and just filling our lives with love and security. To my brother Ricky and niece Helena, for always caring and supporting me.

Thank you indeed to the people who believed in me. Everyone from friends to my GP and my counsellor have all supported me. Their confidence and faith gave me the inspiration to keep writing and finish this book.

Lastly, but with great affection, I would like to thank my dad who is no longer with us. He died many years ago now and way before I got Multiple Sclerosis. He taught me to have the strength and conviction I have today. He never gave in and devoted his life to better things for his family. I follow in his footsteps.

About Multiple Sclerosis

There is a somewhat chequered history to Multiple Sclerosis with the first clearly recognisable case being recorded in the early nineteenth century. The description of the disease has varied substantially over the years. By many in the medical world, it is widely recognised as an autoimmune disease. This is hugely challenged by others, including some medical practitioners, and more so as research takes place and pioneering treatments herald positive outcomes. I have been party to some of those treatments and so for me the jury is very much still out on what category Multiple Sclerosis falls into.

With the many theories rising to the surface about MS, it feels some time away before there are more answers than there are questions. What is agreed on is that Multiple Sclerosis is an unpredictable disease that affects individuals very differently. There is no known cure for it and it is a chronic disease, which will stay with the person diagnosed for the entirety of their lives. It affects more women than men and the age of diagnosis is most commonly between twenty and forty years, although there are exceptions. I find that fact very hard-hitting as the disease strikes so many people at such an early stage of their adult life. I see myself as one of the lucky ones, being thirty-nine years of age when I was diagnosed.

Symptoms can be both diverse and confusing at the best of times. Some of the more common ones include extreme fatigue, numbness and tingling, blurred and double vision, memory problems and walking difficulties. Bowel and bladder changes are also common symptoms as well as being extremely difficult to cope with and manage. The list is endless and the symptoms can be different each day and for everyone. This is a very complex part of the disease to understand. It is indeed demanding, confusing and upsetting for the person with MS. What your body feels like and can perform on any given morning is no indication of what it will be like or be able to do in the afternoon of the same day. There are constant changes and that can be very troublesome to live with. That is the case for the person with MS as well as their surrounding family and friends. It demands a great deal of patience and understanding. Above all it requires adaptability, which is something I have grown into and tried to master the art of. I have succeeded at least to some degree whereby my life is more manageable.

The prevalence and causes that may be attributed to Multiple Sclerosis are complicated and often conflicting. There are numerous studies, which support varying theories. One often raised is that a lack of vitamin D may cause or contribute to the onset of MS.[1] I was personally told, soon after my diagnosis, that I had a chronic deficiency in vitamin D. It is also widely suggested there are real links between diet and intake of saturated fats and the levels of Multiple Sclerosis in different regions. In

1 www.nhs.uk: NHS Choices, Health news, Low vitamin D levels linked to increased multiple sclerosis risk, 27.08.2015

countries with lower saturated fat intake the rates of MS are often reported as significantly lower, particularly in fishing communities.[2]

The most common type of MS is relapsing and remitting (RRMS), which is my own personal diagnosis. There are others, but this one is the most widely occurring type and is identified by flare-ups and attacks of symptoms followed by periods of remission. With no known cure, conventional treatments are themselves sparse. They currently do not offer to treat the disease itself, but only to try to reduce the number of attacks a person has and then try to improve the speed of recovery following a relapse.

There has been research[3] to support the theory that some autoimmune diseases can be triggered after giving birth. Foetal cells can remain inside the mother's body after the baby is born. In some women this can be harmless, but in others it has been considered this may cause confusion in her immune system during the postpartum period, subsequently triggering an autoimmune disease as the immune system attacks itself. One of those is known to be Multiple Sclerosis. Although this theory is not proven and requires a great deal of research, it was proposed to me as the possible explanation for the onset of my MS. It would be very difficult to say with absolute certainty what

---

2 *The Multiple Sclerosis Diet Book*: Chapter 2, p. 10, Dr Roy Swank, Bantam Doubleday Dell Publishing Group, Revised Edition, 1998

3 www.naturopathiccurrents.com: The Postpartum Period – Incidence and Risk Factors of Autoimmune Diseases, Jessa Landmann, ND, 30.04.2015.

happens inside a woman's body during each individual's afterbirth process. What I do know, however, is that something dramatic changed inside my body forever after Elliot was born.

Multiple Sclerosis is a very intimidating disease: it is difficult to predict its path and control it. I have, in my journey, managed to find ways to do the latter. It takes commitment and hard work, but there are ways out there to mitigate this erratic condition.

In the Beginning

'You have to believe in yourself.'

(Jeff Rich)

I was born in 1967. Brought up in the east end of Glasgow, the youngest of four children, I had a great childhood and it was one filled with lots of wonderful memories. I would say it was a pretty sheltered childhood considering the housing estate I grew up on. We grew up very close and shared a real wholesome family life. My youth was spent playing sport almost to the exclusion of everything else, even reaching the accolade of international netball player! There were life's trials and tribulations, but my overriding memory was that of unconditional love and security. Growing up and becoming independent changed everything. I was presented with hurdles and finding a way over them relied on my own resources. I was relatively well equipped from all my positive and reassuring childhood experiences and that has stood me in good stead for what I have had to face in life.

After I graduated at nineteen years old, I decided to move to London to find work and start a new adventure. It was a wonderful adventure that lasted more than ten years. It took me from my first job working in the Civil Service and after that I went on to do a Post Graduate

Certificate in Primary Education. I became a teacher and went on to teach in London for some six years. I had a very rich cultural experience as well as having my eyes opened to a whole new world out there. During the years I spent in London, I lived in Brixton for the majority of the time. I grew very much as a person and played host to a broad range of adventures day and night. Life was about fashion, fun and feeling fabulous at that time. I very much fitted the high-heeled party girl label that was attached to me!

I settled into some routine while living in London over such a long time. My great interests were the gym and exercise classes. I was never away from Brixton Recreation Centre and one exercise class rarely sufficed. I think I bordered on having an exercise addiction and was certainly far too obsessed with my body weight. But it was London after all and I was not alone with my obsession! I firmly described myself as a Londoner for many years. Living there for ten years very much shaped the adult I became. A small piece of me will always belong there.

My years in London gave me the desire and impetus to go further afield to see and do more in other places. After ten years, I figured it was time for a move. I got a teaching job in an international school, in a charming town just outside Barcelona called Sitges. It was by the sea and only a short train ride into Barcelona. I had the most wonderful of times. I worked hard and I played hard. Week days and school nights were focussed on school work and activities, while weekends brought a more party flavour with them! My considered decision to move abroad was a good one. It brought with it a truly awesome lifestyle in the sun with plenty of opportunity for nightlife and travel. Teaching in an international school was a wonderful experience and I learned so much. At that point in my life not only was the future unknown, but I never gave it so much as a glance. I lived every minute in the moment. I had the best of times and my glass was overflowing. London and Barcelona were immense places to live and I enjoyed every minute. I worked and 'played' with some great people and enjoyed all the things that both big cities had to offer. I always had visitors and that only encouraged burning the candle at both ends.

My return home was prompted much earlier than anticipated. My father became very ill with cancer. Once I knew the extent of his illness I took the decision, with immediate effect, to resign from my teaching job and leave Spain. I headed back home to be with him and my mum. I was very glad I made that decision and so quickly. My dad died only ten days after I arrived back home. That took a great toll on the whole family. I found myself back in Glasgow after some eleven years away. I had no job, little money and was living with my mum again. Not to mention I was grieving and it hurt more than I ever imagined possible. I struggled to get work initially, but eventually got a position supply teaching with some help and guidance from my childhood teacher, Miss Bristow. She was a head teacher in the local area where my mum lived. It was kind, considerate and most welcome of her to help. With the rest of my time I turned my attention to exercise again. I joined a gym and religiously went every day. I focussed myself on that and it was a big part of my grieving journey.

Time passed and I moved into my own flat in Glasgow, eventually getting a permanent teaching post outside of mainstream education. It was around the same time I met Allan. We didn't waste much time before we moved in together. We met in May of the year 2000 and moved in together in June of the same year. I have always been an impulsive person. I don't weigh up the options or spend time deciding on things. If it feels right, I've always just gone ahead and done it. I had no hesitation on that occasion and it turned out to be the right thing to do. That has not always been the case with my decision-making – or relationships for that matter!

Allan and I started the whole 'burning the candle at both ends' thing again. We had an awesome time together. So much so that one day an engineer arrived to cut off my electricity because I hadn't paid my bill. I stood at the door and said to him, 'Sorry, I've fallen in love, do you take credit cards?'

It was a few years before we decided we would try and have a baby together. We lost our first baby and it was a terrible time in our lives. We were just filled with sadness and grief and it seemed like it would never end. It did bring us closer. Allan and I have always been strong in tough times and stuck together. We are a formidable team. Only six months later I found myself pregnant again.

The Birth

'The instant of birth is exquisite. Pain and joy are one at this moment.'

(Madeline Tiger)

It was 3rd April 2006 when I was induced into labour. After fourteen uncomfortable hours and still no sign of baby Elliot the decision was made to carry out an emergency caesarean section. It was a long time in labour and very eventful. Nothing on this earth could have prepared me for that experience. Minute by minute brought greater shock and tremendous anxiety. The pain came in waves and the time elapsing between them got less and less, but I was still no further dilated than after the first couple of hours. The midwives could not understand why Elliot was not making his way into the world. After much worry, panic and pain a senior midwife made the decision to do an immediate scan, prompted by the loss of the baby's heartbeat on the monitor. Elliot was discovered to be what is called 'face presenting', so he was stuck and could not make his way out. Overwhelming pain and absolute panic, as my unborn child's life was in danger, was the most frightening moment of my life. It was as close as you could ever imagine to being impossible to cope with. The pain had to stop as I threw the entirely useless gas and air mouthpiece to the ground. Elliot was in a very unsafe position and had been there undetected for many hours. The nursing staff had continued with the inducing process, it seemed, without any due attention to my lack of dilation and progress towards delivery. In a matter of seconds, I was on the ice-cold operating table and the caesarean section was under way. At 11.56 pm, all 10lbs and 3oz of baby Elliot finally arrived. It had been a long and traumatic journey, but the most worthwhile of my life. Allan and I could not have been happier. We were so relieved that he had arrived safe and well. He did look as though he had been through a few rounds in the boxing ring after his troublesome journey to enter the world!

The following morning, I noticed almost immediately that how I was feeling physically was not in any of the maternity books I had read, nor ever mentioned by any midwives or other mums. I could hardly stand upright by myself and could barely move. I just put it down to the harrowing labour and rushed caesarean. There seemed no other logical reason. It is impossible to say otherwise why my physical reaction felt so extreme. It would be true to say though that I have never felt the same in my body since that day.

Allan was due to arrive in a couple of hours and so I arranged to go for a shower. At most I had around two hours' sleep. It was only just morning time and I had been through that emergency caesarean ordeal some seven hours previously. I was shocked as I tried to manoeuvre myself from the bed along to the shower room. Obviously

I was in pain, tired and weak. But as I tried to walk from a standing position I was practically unable. I did not anticipate that. I had to walk along using the wall and take what could only be referred to as baby steps to get there. Exhausted, I had to shower sitting down and could not at that point imagine any way back to where baby Elliot lay sleeping. The nurse brought me a metal chair and put the shower on for me. I sat there and cried as the lukewarm water hit off me and was unable even to lift my arm. It was an excruciatingly slow process and in the end, I called for a nurse to help me back to the ward just by shuffling along. She literally guided me by my arm. It was in fact only around fifteen steps from the shower room back to Elliot, but it took some considerable time to get there. The nurse told me not to worry as it was only hours after my operation and difficult birth, but it still did not sit comfortably with me. I had never heard of anything remotely similar to what I was experiencing. My legs felt completely different and as though they were disconnected from the rest of my body. They were heavy and cumbersome from that day on.

I never told anyone at the time about my experience that morning. After all it was a time of elation and celebration as baby Elliot had just arrived in this world! We had almost instantaneously forgot about his somewhat dramatic entrance as we were consumed with joy, relief and expectation. But somewhere in a little compartment in the back of my mind there remained the unanswerable question as to what had truly happened to me that day. Doctors, midwives, family and friends all pointed to my caesarean for months to come to explain symptoms that would appear, as well as changes in my body and decreasing ability. I was never even slightly convinced, but I had nothing else to go on in those early, vulnerable days. I knew something had changed that day, but what I did not know was that it had changed forever.

It was time though to put those thoughts to one side. All the family were coming to meet Elliot and I could hardly believe I was there with my own, very wonderful baby boy! I got myself dressed, albeit with difficulty. Elliot was to some extent awake by now and marginally content in his little hospital trolley, at least for the time being. I was exhausted and bemused as to what was going on with my body. I had to separate that from the practical on-goings. I was awaiting Allan's arrival sometime very soon and even in amongst how I felt, that was still very exciting. I needed to get little Elliot changed. Due to my inability to move much, as well as the fact I still had a catheter in from the caesarean, I thought I would ask a nurse to help me. It was a hospital after all. It was simply to collect the nappy and wipes from the other side of the ward, not to change Elliot as I wanted to do that myself, despite how I felt. I was stunned when she replied 'no' and commented that the nurses were not there to do things for my baby that I should do myself. I was only asking for a modicum of help considering how bad I felt and what I had been through a few hours earlier. But the answer was a firm 'no' that will always stick in my memory and I had to somehow make my way, in great pain and with my catheter, across the ward. I really was having a challenging day! I put it down to the fact she was an agency nurse and not one that belonged to the ward itself. There was also the possibility that the early morning nurse handover of patient information hadn't paid any attention to detail from the night before!

Fathers could join us on the ward from 10.00 am. As the clock struck exactly ten o'clock that morning a tired but elated Allan strode into the ward with the most beautiful bouquet of flowers. I cannot express my mixed emotions of joy and relief. I could now relax, as Dad was there to take over. The pressure just lifted from me and I looked on as the super-confident Allan gave Elliot his first bath, under supervision of course! All my immediate family as well as my best friend Alison arrived later in the day. Allan and I, along with our new son, had a lovely day together despite my physical ails. Not to mention the fact we were in the corner of a six-bedded ward, with the six newborn babies all expressing themselves! We still had a close and bonding day together. I didn't get to move around much and when I did it was painful to watch me. But my memory is of a lovely day.

Each day passed and I was recovering in some way from the caesarean operation. At the same time, there were other things becoming noticeable, mainly my exhaustion and difficulty with mobility. Those were being put down to post-operative problems and a chronic lack of sleep. I needed to get home. I could not understand why they were making me stay in the hospital. I had to do everything myself. I was in a lot of pain and getting virtually no sleep. We had been in hospital for five long and rocky days, finally making it home on the Friday afternoon. I was discharged after a lot of grumbling on my part.

As the slow days passed back at home we were trying to settle into being a new family of three. We had the usual sleepless nights and tiring days. We loved it and Elliot became very settled now that he was home. I had got to grips with breastfeeding and Allan was good at just about everything! But there were little things niggling at me, particularly the cold numbness around my abdomen where the doctor had cut me. It was that matter which kept leading us back to linking my unpredictable symptoms with the caesarean. I was so, so tired. Then again, isn't every new mum? Allan was tired too. We carried on for a couple of long weeks. We had eager visitors, went out shopping for baby clothes and took Elliot to meet family and friends. We were managing relatively OK, but all the time I felt that my extreme tiredness did not match what others had described. It felt puzzlingly different to me. But, once again, I had nothing to compare it to and no idea that it really was something with the alarming potential that transpired.

2

Getting Worse

It was just another Saturday afternoon in early May. I was casually walking back from lunch with my sister. Elliot was very content lying in the carry-cot part of his pram as he was only a few weeks old. It was a lovely sunny day in May so we decided just to stroll back home as we were all enjoying the spring weather. I was going through a very slow recovery from the caesarean birth and had not yet fully recuperated. I was still weak and feeling unwell, but nothing more significant had happened. My ability and mobility were reduced, but that was to be expected post-operation and post-birthing trauma. I was extremely tired, again not unusual given I had a newborn baby and was breastfeeding on demand. I did have an underlying feeling though that many things were proving more difficult than they should have been.

I thought that some light exercise would support my recovery. The Italian café was only around a mile from where I lived. Although a little tired we were managing slowly as we were in no rush. We had walked just over halfway back to my apartment when, without any warning, it struck me for the first time ever that I may not be able to make it home. My legs were struggling to carry me. They just would not take the messages my brain was sending them and were not going where I asked them to. The best way to describe it would be to go from being completely sober to being completely drunk. There was no warning or gradual build-up. My red pram was the only thing that kept me upright and moving forward. I was so confused, bewildered and frightened. The body that you rely on and take for granted was not doing one of its most basic functions: walking. My initial thoughts were back to post-operation and that my body had not fully recovered. How wrong I was. I was never to walk normally again.

With the support of the pram and my sister helping me stay upright I kept going until I reached my apartment. I was helped step by step as my body completely failed me. The pram was all that was between me and the pavement. I still had to face three flights of stairs, behind the green entrance door, on arrival at my block of flats. I had the bannister to help me and my sister took charge of getting Elliot upstairs. With some assistance, from a very shocked Allan, I reached the top of the stairs exhausted and shaken. I had to compose myself by lying down and leaving Elliot with his dad immediately. I was uncomfortable stretching out on my bed at such an early hour in the day, but I had no choice. I told Allan to bring Elliot into the bedroom whenever he wanted to be fed. As I lay still on my bed I began to notice a numbness spreading from my right foot up through my leg. That was extremely alarming and I lay there thinking, *What the hell is going on?* It was not long until it started on my left foot. Both feet were unnervingly cold and my initial feeling was to freak out, but I would not disturb Elliot in that way and Allan's older son, Michael, was staying with us that weekend. I had no idea how to tell Allan without engendering panic in him. I spoke little for the rest of that evening. There was a burning sensation in my stomach throughout the night. I chose to play it down and internalise my fear, but how I got to sleep I will never know. I did feel overwhelmingly exhausted and that helped. I sensed that night there was something more sinister wrong with me. It was only Saturday and it was what felt like a long time over the weekend until I could see a doctor on the Monday morning. I could do nothing but wait and hope that the feeling in my legs and feet came back to me. But it never did and they have remained the same ever since that day.

Doctors' appointments were available from first thing on Monday morning. By that time, I was suffering from the most shocking exhaustion. I hid under the umbrella that all new mums were very tired, hoping against hope that was the case. I carried with me a really heavy burden from that time onwards and could safely say many days were a 'slog' to get through. My appointment was to see a locum doctor on that day at my surgery in the south side of Glasgow. He put it all down to post-operative symptoms and that my extreme fatigue was due to still taking strong painkillers. How any of that would cause me to lose feeling in my feet and legs I had no idea. But I dutifully accepted his explanation and returned home vowing never to take another one of those painkillers. If it had only turned out to be that simple. He contacted the surgery's health visitor to alert her to the fact I needed more support. In his medical opinion, I had been overpowered by motherhood and all it brought with it and my body was physically drained. I was open to any support on offer, but I was also very aware there was a specific physical element to my difficulties that needed to be addressed too.

No more than two days passed and I was back at the surgery. The numbness from my knees down was by now prolonged. Panic had set in. At that appointment the tears streamed down my face. I was confused as to what was happening to me. I could not feel my lower right leg or part of my left one. I had just had a baby. What the hell was wrong with me? It was my own doctor that time who told me I was suffering from post-natal depression and that would explain my extreme emotions! Admittedly I was very tearful and upset, to the point of being more vocal than normal. I had been reduced almost to my hands and knees getting to the surgery. If it hadn't been for leaning on Allan literally, as he took my full weight, I would not have been able to make it to the appointment. I replied abruptly that I was in fact crying so badly because I could not feel my feet and legs or walk without support. That was certainly not in any of the pregnancy and post-natal manuals I was aware of! Surely that could not be related to post-natal depression? Yet still my doctor made it clear that I did not have any neurological condition. I was angry and confused, not to mention terrified. I had a newborn baby at home and could scarcely walk.

I was suffering from the most overwhelming fatigue. It rendered me incapable of being able to move much.

Everyone was just guessing now as nothing was making any sense. I went home with Allan's help and was left to remain scared and unsure. I was speculating and looking up all my symptoms on the internet. That was mixed in with post-caesarean after-effects and life with a newborn baby. During all of that, my overriding feeling about my health was of fear and pending gloom. I was learning to live life as a first-time mum and tackle all the things you have to do when you have a newborn baby. I spent part of my day ecstatic with Elliot, so filled up with joy and greatness. The other half I was paralysed by fear as I knew there was something physically wrong with me. It is only fair and honest to say that my mum was around a lot in those early days and Allan was too, as much as his work at the time would allow.

When the Google searches returned on more than one occasion Multiple Sclerosis, it began to seep in that maybe my symptoms could be those of MS. The timing just after Elliot had been born seemed impossible, but I had the symptoms. They continued to worsen and again pointed to MS. That time it was a weakening and loss of sensation in my left arm. It became hard to even chop things and certainly unsafe. I struggled to grasp items and there was a great reduction in my fine motor skills. You need your arms and hands ordinarily, but when looking after a small baby those were my necessary tools. I had great difficulty buttoning Elliot's babygro from then on. It felt much more worrying and scary losing mobility in my arm than my leg. Not the sort of comparison you want to be readily making. I returned to see my own GP to explain the fresh symptoms and how they seemed to be pointing in a neurological direction. She replied to me quickly and concisely saying, 'You do not have Multiple Sclerosis.' How could she have been so certain? How could she have been so wrong? It seemed too far-fetched at that point for the medical world to link my symptoms to anything other than post-natal and post-operative factors.

That was until I made an appointment with the head doctor of the practice only days later. He listened intently and asked me more direct questions. I did not cry at that consultation and was not feeling the same panic-stricken way. I had taken myself in hand and realised I had to be strong as well as more assertive and focussed in order to gain the respect and support of the medical world. I answered the questions honestly and calmly. The doctor must have been aware it was my fourth visit in days. He recognised my need for answers and to reduce my panic. Following our discussion he confirmed his medical opinion, commenting to me, 'It's looking good for MS.' Not exactly how I would choose to deliver such news, but nonetheless he had delivered. He was fairly upbeat about it and went on to say he had many patients with MS who lived full and active lives. I did not leave that consultation upset in the same way I had been at previous ones. I felt that at last someone was treating my symptoms with the seriousness they warranted. The doctor suggested some follow-up examinations. That consultation was a real contrast from the other ones with different doctors at the same practice. For the first time, someone else thought it may be a new medical problem I was experiencing and not just my emotional and mental health after having a baby. I was strangely relieved, despite his possible prognosis. There was though an element that the whole situation was surreal, as I tried to make the transition from new mum to possibly someone with a chronic disease. How could that have happened in such a short space of time?

I made one further appointment for a lengthy and rather intrusive examination with yet another doctor. That appointment did not fill me with confidence that I would be treated with respect and care over the coming investigations. The doctor examined me in a cold and impersonal manner. It really did feel like life was going horribly wrong at that point. Instead of being wrapped up in my baby joy, I found myself at the hands of the medical profession and having to accept whatever service they offered. It was symptomatic of the cold and lonely medical journey that lay ahead.

Following that appointment, I was referred to the neurology department at the Southern General Hospital in Glasgow, where Elliot had been born only weeks earlier. I never saw that one coming! We went from absolute joy at the highest point of our emotional journey through life, to a state of shock and riveting fear in a matter of weeks. I was informed that I would have to wait between eight and ten weeks for my appointment with a neurologist. Meanwhile we had to live a difficult life day by day and try as best we could to carry on with our plans for that summer. I tried to put the thought that it could be Multiple Sclerosis to one side. After all, there was no certainty as to what it was and I was still focussed on trying to recover from the caesarean operation and its aftermath. I had a bouncing baby boy to nurture and cherish. Let's just say that even though deep down I thought it was a neurological problem, the other option was the preferred one. I would stay positive. Life with Elliot was so special and I managed to wheel him from room to room in his pram. I had been unwell every day of his life so far. I did not have mixed emotions about life with Elliot, all was joyous with him and I had to be able to endure my physical difficulties to look after him. There was no time or place to feel sorry for myself or give in to my symptoms. It was just not something I ever considered. The only feeling I allowed myself was that of fear. It was so powerful I could not stop it.

Allan had been a great partner up until then, but he was fast becoming a rock that was so steady and supportive. Becoming parents together made us into a stronger team, but going through that journey made us unique in how we loved each other. Allan worked at the University of Glasgow at the time. He had been employed there for some years before Elliot was born. He had taken what leave he could and worked from home when he was able to. When it was time for Allan to go back to work that meant significant consequences for me, particularly in those early days. It was a case of him getting up and out the house first thing of a morning to accommodate his travel across the city. The earlier he left, the better it was to avoid traffic delays. That left me and Elliot at home together for long days. Something that most new mums would relish. When I was pregnant with Elliot I had dreamt of those times ahead. When they had arrived, I wasn't well enough to do most of the things I had planned. Some days were better than others and I always tried to do something with Elliot. I managed on more days than not and usually with the help of my mum and sheer determination.

Allan would be out all day at work. I survived as best as I could. Elliot was only weeks and months old and so it was a very treasured time between mother and baby. Having just become a mum I had so many aspirations and plans. But new symptoms would appear as and when without any warning, playing havoc with those plans. Tingling and what would best be described as 'pins and needles'-like feelings would just occur randomly on any part of my body. Both my lip and eye would tremble rapidly, particularly after exertion, and that would then disappear as quickly as it came. Fatigue arrived as and when it wanted to. Despite all my desires and good intentions, my energy was always painfully low. My balance let me down time and time again. Together it was a lot to deal with and left me feeling perplexed and shaken. I was disappointingly agitated for far too much of my precious time with baby Elliot. After Allan had left the house each morning, I just had to get on with the day alongside Elliot as best I could. I was very much someone who would send out the message that I was coping fine.

Allan's job took him mostly around Scotland and involved overnight stays away. There was nothing we could do about that. It was pressure for both Allan and me in different ways. Sometimes I look back and just don't know how I managed in those early months. But I did. My sister could not come around enough to spend time with Elliot, so she was often there to help. Gran would come over and stay on many a day. My memories of those days, although they were drenched in fatigue, are still of many happy ones. I loved my time with Elliot and even though we were restricted in what we could do and where we could go, it was still a cherished time in my life. It would be dishonest to say that fatigue didn't get in the way. I always wished I had more energy and was more able. But I didn't and those were the cards I was dealt. I did my best.

Allan would always come home as early as he could. He lived in a cloud of guilt at that time. He could see how wiped out I was when he got home, but there was nothing he could do to change the situation. It was often stressful and seldom comfortable. Elliot was well cared for and had so much attention coming his way all the time. We had the summer ahead of us, and the wait for my neurological referrals to be responded to.

3

The Apartment

'He knows not his own strength that has not met adversity.'
(Ben Jonson)

Our apartment was up three flights of stairs. It was an older tenement building in Glasgow so there was no lift. We had lived there for some five years before having Elliot. But we were both fit and healthy and the stair journeys with lots of carrying to and from didn't faze us at all. Our plan was to stay there for the first couple of years of Elliot's life. Only when things were settled would we think about moving house. Firstly, we had to make the inevitable adjustment financially to my returning to teaching on a part-time basis. That was the plan at least.

Since the very first day my feet and legs went numb, I have had difficulty with walking. That meant climbing the apartment stairs was troublesome too. That was most certainly an obstacle I did not need. For the first few weeks I managed, but it took its toll. All the time we were hoping and believing it would just go away one day. With each week that passed it became more difficult to continue living in a third-floor apartment. It is only fair to add that, although fraught with difficulty, I did manage to go out on some days. I would leave the pram at the bottom of the stairs for Allan to lift up on his return from work. My mum would carry Elliot upstairs. I did on occasion 'bump' the pram up the three flights. I collapsed on the sofa when I got inside the apartment and baby Elliot had to wait in his pram until I had recovered somewhat. It was excruciatingly difficult, but still possible. The show had to go on and it did. We went out as much as we could with the pram for a walk or to our post-natal mother and baby group. I remember going to the group one day when Elliot was only weeks old. I asked the midwife who was in attendance if she had known any mums before who had lost feeling in their feet after a caesarean section. I will never forget the look on her face. I think she thought I was somewhat unhinged! The answer not surprisingly was no. I was desperate at the time!

We completed an enlightening baby massage course together when we still lived in the apartment. I didn't stop to think of the challenge it presented. I just pushed on and did whatever had to be done. It was with great difficulty I would try to lay Elliot on his mat. I was terrified as to what was going on with my body, but I carried on regardless in what would be my usual stubborn way. I had to get myself from an unstable standing position to floor level. There was the addition of a small delicate baby and my balance issues. I would twist and turn rather awkwardly. I moved a bit like the Tin Man, and my landings were not pretty. But I got there nonetheless. By the time it came to getting up I was stiff like cardboard and any bends were never smooth! I managed it all because I had the pram to roll everywhere with me and out of sheer stubbornness. I also had a big dose of not caring what anyone thought of me. That has been my greatest ally throughout the years. I always kept going and the pram literally kept me upright and straight. The pram also meant I didn't have to carry anything and had somewhere always to rest little Elliot.

There was one occasion I had taken Elliot for a walk in his pram. We stopped at a local café for a well-deserved coffee and an eagerly sought-after rest. Elliot lay comfortably in his pram, content enough to be out and about. I passed a most enjoyable half hour sipping my cappuccino, whilst fondly entertaining Elliot, with an eager eye on his every expression and movement. Those moments meant everything to me and were just reward for anything else I had to manage in between times. As we were contentedly making our way back home together it suddenly struck me that I had an impending bowel movement. That came entirely without warning and I felt immediate panic that it was imminent. Speed was not possible with my restricted walking and mobility, but I manoeuvred myself with the pram in the direction of my apartment as swiftly as I could. It would be safe to say parts of my body were rigid with panic and that only served to make me more unsteady and slower with my movements.

When I reached the apartment building I could not think of how I would manage to get upstairs with Elliot quickly enough. It was one of the most upsetting feelings I have experienced. Panic, fear and complete helplessness. I kept on trying and trying and it simply raised the level of alarm and anxiety I already felt. I got to the first floor and with still two more to go I could not make it any further. I simply could not believe this was happening. I did not stop, but simply carried on up the stairs, now more in a state of shock than panic.

I got into my apartment still in a state of shock. I strangely did not react in any way outwardly. I simply showered whilst entertaining Elliot, still tucked up and being vocal in his pram by that point. I carried on with my day and didn't utter a word to anyone about what had happened. The only thing I did was a Google search of bowel dysfunction and alongside my other symptoms, it returned the highest possibility yet that it could be Multiple Sclerosis.

After that happened, on top of the other physical complications, I put it to Allan that we may have to think fast about moving. I was managing the groups and classes with Elliot as well as looking after him. But if we could just take the issue of the three flights of stairs out of the equation that would undoubtedly assist me. My mum was offering great support, but had a long journey across the city as she lived in the east end and I was south of the river at the time. Her help and input were invaluable. Most new mums need support and it is great if Gran can be about. That had more of an essential requirement to it for me. Gran was however a willing support and did not let us down. She was there day in and day out.

We would have to consider moving to a new housing estate as I was not well enough to take on any project or do any renovations. With all of that in mind I trawled the internet and, far quicker than anticipated, found a suitable candidate. It was no more than two miles from where my mum lived. It was being built at that very time and would be ready in a little over three months to move into. All we needed to find was the £750 deposit to secure it. The next day Elliot was dropped off smiling and eager to see Gran, as we travelled on to visit the site. There was only a small Portakabin with a precarious ramp. I had to grit my teeth to manage the difficult conditions underfoot of a building site. We were only speaking to the sales assistant for a couple of minutes. Without even glancing at a brochure we agreed to take the next available plot and handed over the cash deposit. That meant just taking the house as it was with no input into its internal design. I had no interest. All I could think about was how quickly I could move to alleviate some of the burden that had befallen me. The sales assistant looked surprised that we didn't investigate further. It wasn't a case of not wanting to, but plain and simple not being able to. She said we could choose the location of a plot and then our kitchen and bathroom design. Not interested. I just wanted to move house and as soon as possible. Anything cosmetic held no importance for me. Moving house was going to be another mountain to climb I could have done without and I just wanted to get on with it. We still had over three months ahead of us with no relief on our daily life on the third floor. But at least now we had an end date in October. Where the house would be located and what the internal design was, I would find out then. It would be fine. Just away from those ghastly three flights of stairs would suffice.

4

A Busy Summer

'Fall seven times. Stand up eight.'

(Japanese proverb)

There was no let-up in my symptoms, day in and day out. Elliot was only weeks old and it was tough going. We all needed a break and time to recuperate together. We had clumsily scheduled for a busy summer that year, without giving it due thought and consideration. But, despite everything that was going on there was still excitement at the family times ahead with our newborn baby boy. We wanted to enjoy and relish those precious few months. There was a much-needed holiday in a cottage in the Lake District, booked for early July. On our return from the cottage we had planned to get married at a small, low-key wedding. It was short notice after having baby Elliot, but we did not know what was in front of us when we made the plans. Elliot would be just over three months by the time the holiday came around. I hadn't done much organising for either occasion. Getting through each day was as much as I could manage.

The marriage proposal had been borne out of our trip to register Elliot's birth. I had only been home a few days after my caesarean birth when we decided to do it. I was very weak and not at all stable on my feet. Allan could not register the birth by himself as we were not married. In our modern-day Scottish society, I still had to go with him! Even though I was not physically able to, there was no choice as we only have twenty-one days here in Scotland to register a birth. The Registry Office sat at the top of a very steep hill, so I was painfully struggling to make it. Nearing the top, I turned to Allan and said to him rather fleetingly that we should get married! That would have solved the whole problem! That is indeed where the first seed was sown for our marriage. I don't remember exactly, but within a week or so Allan asked me to marry him and I was more than happy to say yes. Not the most romantic of marriage proposals, but definitely the most real and meaningful. We were a happy threesome now and we were pleased to cement that in marriage. Our marriage would not be big, but only about our commitment to each other and jointly to Elliot.

As the weeks dragged past it began to look more and more unlikely that the wedding would take place. The chosen date was not exactly well planned or thought through. We had just picked a random date that summer. We were desperate to get some 'normality' back in our lives. Planning our wedding and getting married would also leave very little room to think and worry about my health. In retrospect, I think it was a way of blocking the anxiety and stress and it gave us a great big happy event to focus on! That was not the reason we made our decision to marry, but we were very much in need of some positivity. Whether it would be feasible to manage the physical demands of a wedding with my health issues never featured in our decision-making. We blindly carried on with our plans, refusing to contemplate that things were so serious or that they were for the longer term.

The first thing facing us though was the holiday. In amongst all the worry and busyness, I hadn't managed to do any preparations for it. The truth is, I was struggling to go. I didn't want to, but I was persuaded. As I tried to shop for our trip to the Lake District, my sister had to call for a chair in the shopping centre as my body refused to carry me. I was so scared and unsure what to do. I was trying to carry on with normal tasks, despite my body's inability to co-operate. I absolutely refused point blank to stop and give in. I struggled to lift my legs at times, but I forced them. With relentless determination on my side and Allan's unwavering belief, the decision was taken to go away for the week and leave everything behind. The old adage was around that maybe a holiday 'would do us good'. Not sure if we were positive or deranged! The wedding planning and related decision-making would have to wait on our return home. We needed nothing less than a miracle to turn things around. We somehow got organised and set off together, Allan and I along with Elliot and Gran.

It was a very different kind of holiday as I struggled to walk for most of it and I was constantly worried about why I was wiped out most of the time. Everyone was still putting it down to the long, difficult labour and caesarean birth. To me it was more than that and I think it was to Allan too. We chose to stay positive and not look too deeply into it, even though the doctor's words, 'It's looking good for MS', sat inside my head the whole time.

We spent the week in what I would describe as possibly the smallest cottage in the Lake District! It was the hottest summer I can remember in 2006. The daily temperature soared past thirty degrees. It was a picturesque cottage in the middle of nowhere. Inside it was small, very small. We manoeuvred in the narrowest of staircases with much difficulty. On arrival Allan had to rearrange the cottage furniture in sauna-like conditions to find space for the travel cot. That was not a good start to his holiday, or ours for that matter! He named it 'Lilliput Cottage' and I'm not sure it was with any fondness! Elliot was only three months old and sweetly unaware of all that was going on around him. I did return home with lots of bruises where I misjudged and hit off almost every corner I took!

We woke each morning and tried another little adventure. Unfortunately, with each day that passed I felt weaker. Allan tried everything possible to make the holiday as enjoyable in the circumstances as it could be. It was so hot all the time. I have the most vivid memory of sitting on a bench overlooking Lake Windermere. Allan had to stop the car literally at the bench to drop me off. He bought us ice cream cones to eat as Elliot sat in his red Bugaboo pram taking everything in across the beautiful lake with all the tourists milling around. I recall looking down at that ice cream in the extreme heat with no idea how I was going to raise it up to my mouth to eat it. I did not have the strength to keep my arm upright. I gave up in the end and Allan had two ice creams that day. I just made out that I didn't feel like having one.

In the evenings at the cottage, I did my best to make things 'normal'. I wanted to achieve minimal worrying all round. I even considered the possibility of trying to find some enjoyment in the holiday! That meant, hard as it was, that I should be positive and cheerful. I knew I could manage, despite my physical state, as Elliot was so loving and content. Allan and my mum couldn't have cared more or done more. So, I would pour a glass of wine early evening, curl up with Allan and Elliot to chat and laugh just like we did best. There was no point making anyone feel worse than they already did and I was so mixed up emotionally as I was a happy, grateful new mum at the same time as all of this was happening.

Later in the week we decided to try another day trip so we drove to a nearby town, Barrow-in-Furness. When we arrived and found a car park I realised I could not in fact get out of the car and walk. I could not lift my legs. They were so heavy and absolutely refused to move an inch. I had to physically manoeuvre them with my hands. That was a first and I think partly because of the unusually high British temperature. I could reasonably have been described as completely 'wrung out'. I had no energy or strength anywhere in my body. That was probably the scariest moment in my journey. I had to share that news with Allan and my mum. It was the most stressful of moments, but I was conscious not to panic anyone. I played the situation down and did not make any fuss or show my fear. Allan and my mum set off with Elliot in his pram to try and find some lunch and bring it back to the car. They were both putting on brave faces, but it was still obvious how concerned they were. This was a fun holiday, sitting in a concrete car park inside the car at over thirty degrees! I sat there and tried to keep a slight smile on my face until they were on their way. I was trying to keep a semblance of normality. Not that the situation had any! I sat there, on my own, reassuring myself that I could still feel both my legs, but I just could not move them. My heart raced, but I still smiled on the outside. Elliot was so small and vulnerable. All I wanted to do was nurture and nourish him, yet there I was unable to even stretch over the car seat to be near him. Once Allan and my mum were out of sight I immediately picked up my mobile phone and called my sister. Looking back that was maybe not too fair on her. After all, she was many miles away in Glasgow and was herself helpless to my news. I used more than a few expletives as I vented both my fear and frustration. What was going on? I knew then that I was very unwell, but what was it?

On their return to the car they brought with them some fresh sandwiches. Allan made the optimistic decision that we should drive closer to the water and have our lunch there. He really was trying to make things all right and a good job he was doing. Elliot was getting a bit restless and unsettled with the heat and spending so much time strapped in the car seat or the pram. The others managed a short stroll with Elliot in the pram, whilst I could only manage to lift my legs out the car door. Nevertheless, it was still a lovely view of the water and I was at least getting some air and a sandwich! You've always got to find the positives, even if it does sometimes mean you need to reach out that little bit further! Gran managed to lose a rarely-used sandal in the water and so a very difficult afternoon ended with some hilarity!

On our arrival back at the cottage it was a little cooler in temperature and Allan took me as close as the car could get to the cottage door. I literally clambered my way inside and got some assistance to make it into the garden, where we all sat for a little while under some shade. The garden was itself a little hill, so things were really going our way! Not! I almost crawled up it and certainly no better than an awkward shuffle. Inside I was slowly dying from this ordeal dressed up as a holiday, but on the outside I stumbled along smiling as best I could and being as active a mum as possible.

Elliot lay on his little rug and tried relentlessly to get on the move! I knew I was going to have to talk to Allan about our planned wedding, which was booked to take place in less than three weeks. I was well aware by that point I was not going to be able to choose a dress or anything remotely like that. I was struggling just to cope with each day and to look after my gorgeous little bundle of Elliot. I took a deep breath as we sat in the cottage garden and suggested for the first time to Allan that we should maybe postpone the wedding. That idea was met with big disappointment and a feeble attempt that somehow it could still be possible. The dejection was written all over his face. It is amazing how we deny ourselves the truth for so long when we are scared. I know I'm rather unconventional most of the time, but going down the aisle on my hands and knees was a bit too much for even me! It was time to face facts. I had to open up, be honest and tell Allan straight that there was no possibility I was going to be able to make it. That was a very sad day and the first time in my life that anything had stopped me doing what I wanted to do. I have always just barged on, but becoming a bride beat me on that occasion! I think Allan knew deep down, but it was not in his nature to give up easily, if ever. We made the decision that day there would be no wedding in July. If I'm honest I was more relieved than disappointed. I was understandably consumed by what was going on with my health and looking after Elliot. I had only reluctantly agreed to go on the holiday. We were grasping at straws trying to keep our dwindling spirits up.

We made a point not to cancel our few wedding arrangements, but to postpone them and the random date of 19th October was set as our new wedding day. That would give me a few months to hopefully recover somewhat. Ridiculously hopeful we certainly were! Soon after our return home we discovered that the entry date for our new house would be the 13th October! What a busy week that would turn out to be. We had a few months ahead of us and the referrals had not yet resulted in any appointments. We had to wait patiently for them.

Daily life continued once we were back home and so therefore did my daily struggle. I coped as best I could. I learned ways to adapt to my circumstances and all life involved now was looking after and cherishing Elliot. We had lots of good times and stayed home more often than we would have otherwise. Any trips were local and short-lived. I managed a few outings to the park with the help of my trusted pram and my mum by my side. Sometimes I ask myself how I survived in those early days. I was in my worst state physically and with such a young baby. But I did. Love and determination can be overwhelmingly powerful.

I even continued to attend the local mother and toddler group, always desperately trying to find someone else who had developed similar symptoms after having a caesarean birth. Even if someone knew of another mum this had happened to and could help shed some light on our unprecedented situation. Anything would help. But no one ever had.

5

An Even Busier Autumn

'In times of great stress or adversity, it's always best to keep busy, to plow your anger and your energy into something positive.'

(*Lee Iacocca*)

We were only a few weeks back from our adventure by the Lakes when I was faced with the return date to my teaching post in the middle of August. It was the beginning of the new school year and my maternity leave was over. I had taken my leave early due to complications in my pregnancy. So, although Elliot was just four months old I was expected back to work as normal. The main difference was that there was just about nothing else normal in my life at that point. I was still considerably unwell and so it was an onerous decision for me. It was also more complicated due to the fact I would start to lose pay if I did not return. It is worth remembering I had just experienced the expense that comes with a newborn baby.

I had been teaching for around five years in a day care unit in Glasgow when I stopped to go off on maternity leave. It was a big difference after ten years' classroom teaching in mainstream schools. The young people had

31

most often either been excluded or refused to attend school. They had turbulent home lives and were very vulnerable indeed. I learned the meaning of resilience through those young people.

Returning to work after my maternity leave would have held its own challenges. But I was very unwell and still waiting on hospital tests to ascertain what was wrong with me. I was clearly not well enough to go back, but I had to give it a try. I had made some improvement since the holiday and I was managing basic tasks. I had to push myself very hard and it was absolutely exhausting. There was also the small matter that I wanted to look after Elliot by myself. But despite everything, the day arrived and I went back to working as a teacher. Looking back, I can hardly believe I even attempted to go, never mind the fact I did. My journey to and from work involved two buses each way, and a long steep set of stairs on arrival. I had to use those stairs throughout the day as the young people needed to be escorted always. I did limit my trips up and down them with colleagues very willing to step in and help. It was a fairly big ask of me given my symptoms and ill health. It was completely exhausting and the hardest physical task of my life thus far. But I pushed myself and went through those barriers relatively unknown to everyone else around me.

It was heart-wrenching enough leaving baby Elliot with his gran. He was so small and vulnerable, but he was in good hands. I was returning to work on a part-time basis, which had always been the plan. The first day was extremely difficult. I was weak, my balance was poor and I was suffering from fatigue. Allan took me in the car on that first day and as many days thereafter as he could. I liked the diversity of the post and being part of a close working team. I was able to pass myself off for the first couple of days. My manager was very supportive and made for a gentle passage back for me. I would travel home at the end of the day with difficulty, as I was beyond tired and very unsteady on my feet. I was still extremely excited to get back to Elliot. Without him around I would have gone straight to lying down on my return home. But as so often in those circumstances, Elliot would serve to lift my serotonin. I was not exactly able to take over from Gran, but I would give it my best shot. She had usually been out on a long walk with Elliot in his pram and thoroughly enjoyed her day.

It was very hard to get up the following day to go back to work. Very hard indeed. After only a few weeks I had no idea how I could go on. I was back in the swing of things and with the full responsibilities of the post. Being part-time made it just possible for those first weeks. I was however finding it an increasingly uphill struggle. On top of that looking after Elliot on the days of the week I didn't work, whilst being the only thing I wanted to do, became more and more difficult. The part-time teaching was rendering me incapacitated to look after him. That was devastating for me. We were under a great deal of pressure. Allan had used up any leave from his work that he could. Gran was amazing, but I was conscious of asking too much of her.

I pushed on into October. I had to face the fact that the time had passed where I had reached my limit. I was only able to manage walking in the workplace as there was always something to hold onto as I passed from room to room. There were no long corridors or passageways. I knew I had to go off on sick leave at least until I had completed my hospital investigations and got the results to find out what was wrong with me. The belief, at the time, was that I would be able to start some treatment that would return me to health. My doctor agreed and I was signed off from work.

From then on I was simply relieved to stay at home. I focussed only on looking after Elliot during the day and my mum came to help as and when she could. That turned out to be more days than not. I muddled by and we got there. It was all very different from what I envisaged and it had all happened so unexpectedly. We took it in our stride and carried on regardless. At least the pressure of working life had been lifted. We spent long drawn-out winter days at home together, sometimes just a day on the floor. Toys, mats, books and cushions. Those were very simple times, but I remember them vividly. I was not capable of much more, but the good thing was Elliot was entirely satisfied with my undivided attention hour after hour. Our bond got stronger and stronger as did his demand for constant attention! It taught me the real joy of simple things in life. A good lesson to learn, especially when you can't reach out to do anything else.

October was a very busy month for us. We had the house move and the rearranged wedding happening and that was surely enough to contend with. It is hard to comprehend all the changes that took place in our lives in such a short space of time. We did not mean for it all to happen in that way, but it did. I think the madness that came with it all kept us going!

As the wedding got closer we were not particularly prepared once again. There was a feeling though that time, 'the show must go on'. I was never going to be on top of things, but I was on that occasion determined to be able to go through with the wedding. It was not going to amount to much more than that, but that would do. It was vital to get some positivity and something to celebrate. I needed to get thinking about some wedding plans and getting organised.

First thing was first. I embarked on a mission to get a dress. That was not going to be easy as I was very limited in how far I could walk and how much energy I would have when I reached my destination. That left only one possible decision, to have my wedding dress made. I met with a dress designer, Lesley, as soon as possible. She was a friend of a friend and without delay we got started. Choosing the dress material presented the first big hurdle. By the time I reached the shop I was exhausted and wanting to lie down. I held on for dear life to my pram as it kept me upright. I surrendered, without protest, to the style and colour of the material. Big mistake. It was a slippery slope thereafter.

Lesley came to the apartment for most of the meet-ups. That helped with my fatigue and mobility issues. There was a lot to do and time was tight, but we were not worrying about that as my dress design was simple and my sister (who was my bridesmaid) had it all under control. At least that was what I allowed myself to think! It was just a small Registry Office wedding with an afternoon meal and my dress was low-key to match the occasion. What could go wrong?

My first actual fitting was arranged to try on the dress. We had started packing for the house move by that point so there were boxes scattered around our apartment. Allan made himself scarce and Elliot was sleeping in his cot. Very excitedly the dressmaker pulled the dress from the bag. My jaw dropped, my heart collapsed. I wasn't a spring chicken, it wasn't a big show wedding, I wasn't at my slimmest post-baby and I wasn't too well, remember. But oh no, that creation was surely not for me. It had grown what could only be described as bows and frills. I hadn't asked for them and they were certainly not in line with the style of dress I wanted to get married in. The standard of craft and skill was exceptional, but it was a very eccentric design which did not match my personality and more importantly at the time, my mood! Lesley was just lovely, but we had clearly crossed our communication wires at some point!

I was moving house in six days and getting married in twelve! I was not going to wear that dress and once everyone realised that, we set to trying to figure out what to do. My first thought was to wear my skinny jeans and white t-shirt. Problem was, post-pregnancy, I wasn't quite skinny enough to get into them! My choices of what to do were limited. I was not physically able to go out dress-hunting and so we had to look at alternatives. We agreed Lesley would go off and make the adjustments I had decided on and that were indeed possible. Lesley would do her absolute best to turn things around.

For me though, I went to bed with a heavy burden that night. Things were not good. I wasn't well most of the time: I couldn't travel very much. Now I didn't have the dress I wanted. I had no decent shoes I could walk in. More accurately, I couldn't walk very well in any shoes! I was in the middle of packing for the house move. I was running out of positivity and most definitely out of ideas. How on earth the situation could be turned around felt beyond me.

We moved out of our flat and into a luxury hotel for two heavenly days in no man's land! A well-deserved treat that went some way to lifting my spirits. That was to allow for flooring to go down and final arrangements for the house move to be made. The 'new' dress was brought to the city centre hotel. It was time to meet it again and try it on. The best way to describe it was that my dress was now wearable, but not much more than that to me. My first mistake had been the choice and colour of material, but that was solely down to my health and inability on the shopping trip. The dress was just a mix of styles and it didn't mix well with me. But at the same time Lesley had done a great job to salvage it as I did not have a plan B. I had an image of a dress in my head and that, I'm afraid, is where it stayed! I did lose a bit of heart, but in the scheme of things it was OK. That was the dress sorted as best it could be under the circumstances. It was time to turn my attention to the house move!

The day arrived and we moved into our new house in the east end of Glasgow. It felt somewhat strange mixed with a little disappointment to be returning to the east of the city where I was raised. I had enjoyed my anonymity for many years and always loved moving on to pastures new, but things were different now and I had to accept the changes. I was so desperate for some relief that it didn't really matter. The most important thing was to try and make all our lives a little easier. We had a removal company to do the heavy work and the house was a new build. Friends and family worked tirelessly to help us get settled by early evening. That was as much attention as we gave the house move. As soon as the house was arranged so that family life could function, it was on to the next thing! The day after we moved in my friend and her family arrived from London for our wedding. So it was down tools and out for a catch-up lunch. It certainly was a busy week! It was just a matter of being swept along with it all and holding on tight to my pram to get from place to place!

Even with only five days to go to the wedding, and just having moved house, I still had the task of finding and buying shoes! I had to be able to walk in them as well as like them. I had to go shopping in the city centre. With the help of my sister, I managed to get a pair of shoes with a heel that I could walk gingerly in. Again, they would not have been my first choice but were, in keeping with my dress, passable. I picked up some fashion jewellery in a one-stop shop before concluding the day with a cold glass of cava. We had earned it and I was trying to put some normality into the whole event. It must have been so difficult for my sister, Allan and close family. Every time there was something nice to do or plan, there I was falling apart. I recall clearly making decisions about having a glass of wine around that period. I felt so drastic and low in energy that it could not possibly make me feel any worse (least that's what I told myself), but maybe lift my spirits? Sitting down together with a glass of wine wholly served to help those around me scratch the surface of normality in otherwise wearisome times. It allowed me to connect with myself and send the signal that I was all right and we could still create nice times in our future. All the shopping was done in one street in Glasgow city centre. I walked arm in arm with my sister to all of three shops with rest periods in between! Then we got a taxi home. Four days to go until the wedding.

The house was full of boxes waiting to be emptied, but they would have to wait. When the doorbell rang the following evening, I opened it to two massage therapists with massage tables in tow stood there! It was all bordering on madness. That was my sister's idea of a hen night. I was not able to go out and do anything so she had arranged that at my house. The same house I had moved into a couple of days prior! First thing was first. The cardboard boxes needed to be stacked to make way for the massage tables. Not my job of course. The chilled bubbly was opened and it was time to forget about everything and enjoy the next couple of hours. If I'm honest I just wanted to curl up and let the world pass me by. Considering that wasn't an option and others had invested so much, I had to somehow rise to the occasion. All that time Elliot, at six months old, blended in with whatever was going on. The more people that were about and things going on, the better it was for him!

Thursday the 19th October 2006 arrived and I needed to be in the best shape possible to manage the day ahead.

I had the hair appointment first to try to make up for the disappointment of my dress. That time it went well and I was happy on my return home. Hair done, make-up done and I felt great, put on my redesigned dress and I dropped down a few notches. I wasn't devastated in any way, it looked all right. I was so grateful to have made it thus far and felt positively confident I was going to make the day. It is amazing how life changes and you realise what's important. Marrying Allan and being well enough to do so with our son was what mattered now, not my dress. Although it would have been nice to have it all! But I was coping!

I felt very much uncomfortable with the idea of walking out to a waiting audience. As it turned out, I was. The short service was more enjoyable than anticipated, primarily down to Allan, who went to great lengths to make sure I was well looked after. The only part I was at ease with was committing to Allan. That was effortless, as I had done so in my head and heart many times before. I felt happy and well. I didn't give a second thought to any symptoms or feelings of being unwell. It was photos next, again I felt awkward. Trying to walk with any grace was an added pressure with my heeled shoes. Luckily it was my wedding day and I could hang on to Allan without arousing suspicion! Only I knew, and my sister, that the dress and shoes were not of my choice. Everyone else thought I'd chosen them and it was my dream outfit. Not. I was aware though that guests shared the same view that my attire was no more than acceptable, as almost no one commented on me as a bride or referred to my dress! Except for Allan and my mum that is. In different circumstances that would have been upsetting, but they didn't know what I had been through or what it had taken to get to where I was. I did and although a compliment would have been nice, I was doing just fine.

Once we arrived at the restaurant, an Italian called Sarti's in Glasgow city centre, I felt I could relax a little. The food and service were exceptional and Elliot was of course the star of the day. I managed to relax, chat and enjoy. By now I was in control of those clumpy shoes and even making unnecessary journeys, albeit short ones with someone by my side! All the friends I had invited came along. I chatted with as many people as I could and felt it was a truly enjoyable afternoon. I was a little more reserved and in the background than I would have normally been. I had good reason for that and it was quite a feat I got as far as I did. Elliot was in great form and loved all the attention. We made our way home late afternoon. We were more than happy with our wedding day. We had Elliot now and that meant a whole different direction for us. We gave him his usual evening bath and put him to bed. He was tired after his big day! Then we sat down to relax and opened a bottle of wine. The only difference that night was that we were married. Not the usual Mr and Mrs. I had decided to stay with my own name. But we were absolutely united in every other way.

6

'A Winter of Discontent'

'Keep calm and carry on.'

(British Government)

October 2006 was a pivotal month in my life. So much happened and throughout everything I was working with a body very much in decline. The previous few summer months had presented us with unprecedented challenges. No one knew what was wrong with me and many others didn't even know I was unwell. We never talked about Multiple Sclerosis much after the doctor's prognosis. I thought a lot about it and was forever searching online. However, it is not uncommon to associate varying health problems with the afterbirth of a baby and the changes that happen to a woman's body naturally. Therefore, everyone held on to that. But I knew subconsciously something had changed forever. Whether I believed it at the time is a different story. Every day I dreamt of feeling my feet and legs again and walking without supreme effort. I would close my eyes and imagine my 'old' life and my 'old' body. I have vivid memories of how much of a struggle it all was. I had to 'move heaven and earth' to be able to get married and move house. But I did manage to do them both despite my physical deterioration. The more I tried to do and the more I managed to do, the better we all felt. It meant we could convince ourselves things were not so bad and there was still hope. I was the only person who knew deep down we were kidding ourselves. There was no other option though than to just get on with life as best we could.

We were married and had moved house. We were unpacking for some time due to everything else that was going on. It took us a long time to settle. To be honest nothing cosmetic held any importance. It never did matter in our lives as we are not materialistic. But we did have a big list of priorities. Right up there at the top was the first hospital appointment, which had arrived for the beginning of November. It would be fair to say we just took life one day at a time. Allan had returned to work and I was relieved I had no pressure anymore to do the same thing. I just had to live and cope day by day, with my circumstances, in the best way possible.

The new house was just behind an out-of-town shopping centre. It became my refuge on as many as three days each week. It was just over the road from the house and on a bus route when necessary. It was an outdoor centre so we got plenty of fresh air. Put another way, here in Glasgow, we got blown to bits! It had a small soft play area, which was normally quiet and so we would spend the morning in there. That play area was always my back-up plan. If we were at home too much or Elliot was unsettled, I would simply put him in the pram and off we would go. It saved me on many an occasion. Elliot would get to play and be amused and it did not require much of me physically to watch over him. The pram assisted me to get there or we took the bus. I do remember arriving at the play area and thinking to myself that if I let go of the pram I would fall over. I would just take it to the nearest seat with me and sit down. No one ever knew and I would just keep smiling as I did it!

Trips like those and sometimes long days in the house were the only ways to pass that winter in 2006. Occasionally as time went on I would travel to the city centre with the pram and meet my mum for lunch. Those days were rare, but they were better days when they did happen. I would sometimes go for acupuncture, whilst Gran roamed with Elliot in his pram. Allan would always arrive home as soon as he could at the end of his working day. There was no choice but to keep muddling through. At least now we were in a house with entry straight from the path. Facilities were far more conveniently placed and the surrounding area was comfortably flat.

As time went on I grew some attachment to our new home. I appreciated the close proximity to my mum and my sister moved in around the corner. My brother lived only a mile away. There were lots of names and faces around from my childhood. Living back in the east end of Glasgow would bring with it some significant lifestyle changes for us all. But I would go on to meet many nice people and I had spent the majority of my life there, so it would not be anything unknown. It was not how I imagined life would turn out. I liked the freedom that came with living further afield. I had thoroughly enjoyed immersing myself in different cultures and lifestyles. But like many things in my life that had changed, adapt and quickly was the message ringing loud and clear to me. There was not a single thing I could do to change anything, so best to dig deep, see the positives and just get on with it! There were plenty of positives, none greater than the few special friends I went on to make. It was also very comforting to know that as Elliot grew up he just loved having family around and the door always knocking. Not sure Allan would say the same!

We had alleviated some of our difficulties. The house move and being signed off sick from teaching were the main reasons for that. Having family close by made the rest of the difference. The time soon arrived for my hospital appointments.

The initial appointment was to meet with the consultant neurologist. He seemed thorough and efficient. He did not however inspire or fill me with much hope. At that point I suppose that was not his job. He referred me for a long list of blood tests. They were testing, in the first instance, for Multiple Sclerosis. To diagnose it is a matter of eliminating other potential conditions first as there is no single laboratory test that can give a positive diagnosis on its own.

It was not long until I was given an appointment for an MRI scan. I appreciated the fact they were treating my case with some urgency as I was a new mum struggling to look after my baby. It felt daunting to go for an MRI and the consultant's description of it left me nervous and unsure if I would be able to cope with the physical surroundings and expectations. It seemed it would be claustrophobic and I had to lie still for at least twenty minutes in an uncomfortably noisy tunnel. Considering the scan was to ascertain whether I had Multiple Sclerosis, there were some serious nerves thrown in too.

I contacted the consultant neurologist to talk over my concerns. He suggested that he would write to my GP and recommend a prescription of Valium I should take on the morning of my appointment. I didn't sleep well the night before the scan. An unsettled baby Elliot woke up in the early hours looking for some milk. I was happy to enjoy his company. In the morning I was not very bright eyed, but that suited my muted mood and desire to be as lethargic as possible. I took the eagerly anticipated Valium before we set off and by the time we arrived at the hospital, I would describe myself as being in a 'marshmallow' state. Most definitely not unpleasant and it very much helped me cope. The time came to part company from Allan and prepare physically for the scan. The room was cold and I've never been a fan of the NHS gown! It is not the most dignified of states and for that reason I was relieved to be on my own. I was refreshingly surrounded by lots of smiling faces as the hospital staff tried in vain to make the whole thing feel all right. The benevolent nurse explained what I had already been told. Straight forward, lie down and remain still. Not that simple, I can tell you. But I had taken the Valium to assist me. As the scanner moved my head under the small tunnel there was the heightened realisation that I was going to find out what was wrong with me. I wasn't sure anymore if that was a good thing. It seemed incomprehensible that, within a matter of months, I had gone from the birth of my bouncing baby boy to lying flat out on an MRI scanner at the absolute mercy of the medical world and its investigations. Everything I had known about myself and my abilities throughout my entire life had changed. I was living in a body I didn't recognise. I was very scared and did my utmost to block any thoughts by making buzzing noises in my head. Very basic I know, but I had to try something to cope. The Valium did its job well and helped render me listless. It was a long twenty minutes, but the nurses were excellent and kept talking to me throughout, assuring me how well I was coping and literally counting down the minutes. It was probably the only time in my life I have emptied my mind. The Valium helped and I had no thoughts during the scan. I was frightened that I would panic. There was immense relief as I heard the words, 'That's you all finished.' I had the gown off and was back dressed with Allan as fast as I could manage. That was not really fast at all! It was unlike me, but I didn't stop to ask any questions as I knew I had a good few weeks to wait for the results. The consultant had given me an appointment for early February and suggested that's when I would find out the results and any subsequent diagnosis.

I needed some time to think and let the Valium wear off before returning home to Elliot. We, unusually, chose to wander around an indoor shopping centre. I felt pretty much detached from the world, but regrettably relieved that my fate was soon to be known. We made our way to the car and were home by lunchtime. Elliot was entertained and happy with his Aunty Maggie as always. We didn't have much to say about the morning except it was over. I was finally on the way to finding out what was causing all the turmoil and difficulties.

I still had my appointment to attend for what is called the Visual Evoked Potentials Test. For that, small electrodes were attached to my head to monitor my response to a variety of tests. I had that appointment within a short space of the MRI. I have never tried or concentrated so much in a test before. Sounds ridiculous I know, but I was trying so hard to stop it being Multiple Sclerosis. At that stage I still held hope and believed I could somehow get better once again. The test was a non-invasive one and passed without any great attention. It was not a big deal in comparison to the MRI. It was time to take a back seat from front line services and investigations at the neurology department and wait for the results.

I recall saying to Allan that for the next couple of months we would not know the outcome and could do nothing more. All the tests to date were completed and we should go ahead and try to enjoy our first Christmas with Elliot. It had been quite a year in our lives. We will always look back at 2006 as the most tumultuous year. So much happened and everything changed. There were more good memories than bad ones and I think that was a reflection of us. We had been met with some mighty challenges and stretched to our limits. But we were still standing at the end of that year. It was the same year we had our son together, married and moved in to our first family home. Suggested by some to be the most wonderful events in one's life calendar. They were so different because of my deteriorating health, but still magical in their own weird and wonderful way.

We decided to live in our little bubble and manage my symptoms whilst trying to have a wonderful first Christmas with Elliot. Ignorance sure is bliss. New Year was to bring with it the news that would change life forever.

7

The News

'Everyone has gone through something that has changed them in a way that they could never go back to the person they once were.'

(Unknown quote)

It was Wednesday 3rd of January 2007. A dull and menacing day in Glasgow. Rain, wind, dark skies and plenty more rain. I had a routine appointment with my then GP. We made our way by bus, myself and baby Elliot, all wrapped up and hiding from the storm. I was wet and cold, but in good enough spirits and waiting to collect only another sick certificate for my employer. We made our way down the narrow corridor into the surgery when we were called. I made my very specific request and the doctor set to writing out the certificate. I was still awaiting, with great trepidation, the results of my MRI scan and not yet able to return to my teaching post.

As the doctor unassumingly floated through my file for information I caught the smallest of glimpses of a headed letter from the neurology department at the Southern General Hospital in Glasgow. The doctor himself hesitated as he glanced over it and then hurriedly moved on. With some assertion, I asked sharply what the letter said. The doctor awkwardly replied that it was information the hospital would soon be getting to me. He made a gallant effort to move on and return our attention to the now insignificant sick certificate. Almost immediately I repeated my request about the letter. The doctor momentarily was clumsy with his words and not clear and confident as he would normally be. I knew right at that moment he had the results of the tests and my diagnosis in front of him. He knew what had been causing my feet to be numb, why I was dropping things, why I was losing my balance, why I was finding it difficult to walk only a few steps and why just putting a few words into a sentence felt like my brain had just run a marathon. I had to know now, even though I instinctively knew it was not good news. The palms of my hands were sweaty and my mouth was becoming increasingly dry. Baby Elliot was quiet in his pram, something you would not normally associate with him. I made my final assertive demand for the information in the letter. Without any thought, I abandoned what would be seen as acceptable etiquette whilst attending a doctor's appointment. I was already panicking inside and now more obviously on the outside. I was insistent and clear that he should tell me right now. It was my information after all. He very quietly and with reservation delivered the blow. He read out many words, of which all I heard were, 'the results are consistent with that of Multiple Sclerosis.'

He continued to talk, but I heard nothing more and without delay I stood up and put my hand on the pram. I made the quickest of exits from the surgery, barely stopping to cover the pram and protect Elliot from the pouring rain. I was in a state of shock and inside my head was chaos. All I could think was, *I have Multiple Sclerosis.* I kept repeating that faster and faster. I just couldn't find anywhere to go with that one thought. I stepped forward then backwards, all the time moving the pram up and down. My very worst fear had been confirmed. There can be no worse feeling than when you get terrible news and you realise for the first time you cannot and will not be able to change it. I've always lived my life believing I was in charge of my own destiny. My thoughts turned around and that seemed no longer to be true. My heart was racing and the rain was still hammering down. By now Elliot was beginning to get restless, he was kicking and wrestling around in his pram. Already I was confronted with a choice. Go into meltdown with my devastating news or comfort and respond to my son and his needs. There was no choice. My journey as a new mum with Multiple Sclerosis had already begun. I took the deepest of breaths and turned the pram around to face our path, both the path in front to walk and now the path that would lead our lives in a very different direction. I looked at Elliot and instantly knew I had the toughest test in front of me: motherhood and Multiple Sclerosis. How would I live with this relentless disease and at the same time raise Elliot the way I wanted to? That was my challenge; there was no choice. All the things I had thought about and made plans for changed in that one moment. As I pushed the pram forward my heart pounded and I knew I was walking into the biggest fight of my life.

As I moved from being in an almost paralysed state my thoughts turned to telephoning Allan with some immediacy. I was walking in the freezing cold and rain trying to find shelter for Elliot in his red Bugaboo pram, but we were exposed to the elements. I decided to pause and phone him anyway. He answered only to be met with a still silence as I tried to gain composure to talk calmly and not to shock. I failed and blurted out, 'It's MS.' My tears were mixing with the rain. Without much more being said I remember him telling me to just head home. He would be back as soon as possible. Cold, wet, broken-hearted and very, very frightened I arrived home. Shortly afterwards the door opened and it was Allan. Little Elliot was so quiet and sleepy now, wrapped in his pram and sheltered from the storm outside, happily unaware of the gathering storm waiting to be unleashed upon our lives, both emotionally and physically. Allan and I hugged in complete silence and held on for a while. Moments later I launched into an explanation about the doctor's file with the letter from the neurology department. We were both of the understanding I was due to attend the hospital the following month in February. That was when we would get told the results of my medical investigations. So, the news came as a great shock to us. We were not prepared for it and had absolutely no idea what to do or even say. I could not take it in as I went over and over it in my mind. We had baby Elliot with us, only nine months old, needing all the care and attention he so lovingly deserved. It was not as though we could explain to him or suddenly focus our attention elsewhere. And so, the platform was set for things to come. Multiple Sclerosis had to know its place from the beginning. No time to grieve or panic. Straightforward 'onwards and upwards' without stopping.

There I was, a new mum, who had been unwell for some time. Since Elliot had been born life had been a real challenge and all the time we held out hope that it was due to the difficult pregnancy and birth. We never stopped believing and hoping it could in some way all be linked to everything that had gone on. No, we had just found out three short days into a new year on the 3rd January 2007 that we were wrong and it wasn't going to go away. We had our gorgeous son Elliot with us for our life's journey and now we had been joined by this big and unknown disease, Multiple Sclerosis.

I had always considered deep down that it was MS, but you never cease hoping. Never. Allan had held on to the thought it was linked to the emergency caesarean section. One of the first signs that there was a problem was numbness and loss of feeling all around my abdomen where I had been cut by the doctor during the caesarean section. Maybe Allan was just hoping too. Nothing prepared me for that day and just wandering around the house, picking up Elliot, changing him, feeding him and all the whilst thinking, *I have MS and I'm going to have it forever.*

Allan phoned the neurology department at the hospital to speak to my consultant. He was enraged I had found out on my own with Elliot. Allan was assured a call back as soon as possible. We paced around the house for the rest of the morning. It was filled with lots of emotions, tears, shout-outs as well as talking and sharing our feelings. Our future now seemed precariously balanced.

I felt an urgent need to find something I could focus on and that immediate desire for hope. I have always believed in taking action over waiting and contemplating. The time seemed right to push aside the flood of dark thoughts, take care of lively Elliot's needs and respond to this sudden invasion of news with some positive, precise action. I decided to go to the book store not far from my house. It was a large store so I could browse and hopefully find a book that would meet my needs. I wrapped Elliot up again and we set off. I needed to find out what I was dealing with and what I could embark on doing to help myself. I hoped the weather would be a little kinder to us as we were having a challenging enough day. Once again, I was wrong. As we stood at the bus stop the rain just kept hurling at us, but Elliot was well wrapped up and far away from all that was going on that day. Allan stayed home waiting for the phone to ring.

We arrived at the book shop. Elliot was not as happy to sit relaxed in his pram anymore. He wanted to be heard. That meant a speedier look than planned at the books available and feeling a little more harassed. That comes with the territory of shopping with babies and young children. You eventually come to terms with it and just buy the first thing you see! I sifted through the many books until I found the small section on Multiple Sclerosis. Most were clinical, medical books that held no interest to me. Why would I want to read what might happen to me in ten, twenty or thirty years? I didn't want to know yesterday how I would grow older and what illness might befall me. I could see no reason for that to have changed today. I've never understood why anyone would read something that would scare the living daylights out of them regarding their own health and well-being. I put my hands on *Multiple Sclerosis; A Self-Help Guide* by Judy Graham. My immediate thought was that it was the right one for me and without any further delay I made my way to the checkout to pay.

On our return home, I could hear Allan on the telephone in a tone of voice that could at best be described as assertive! I got Elliot comfortable with his mat and toys and waited on Allan to come downstairs to join us. We could share our experiences of the afternoon. Undoubtedly, it felt better to take action. Much preferable and more profitable than moping around in tears, panic or sadness. The consultant apologised profusely to Allan whilst explaining that letters are dispatched to GPs with results. It just so happened there were several weeks before my hospital consultation. If I had not attended the GP surgery independently, I would not have found out the way I did. Allan politely suggested that arrangement could be reviewed!

We were now home on a freezing January day trying to digest the news that anyone would fear. I had a lifetime chronic disease to deal with. How was I going to look after my baby and cope on my own when Allan was working away? How could I continue to work and earn money to meet our financial commitments? How could I bring my son up independently with a disabling disease? There were so many questions swirling around in my head. I had a book to read with some urgency. That day and the days that followed, in every spare moment, I consumed another few pages. In the beginning I read it almost with desperation. It is fair to say that none of its content suggested any miracle cure for MS or even how to overcome it. It was a straightforward guide to managing MS and ways in which you could help enhance your quality of life. I was not looking to try any far-out procedures or miracle potions. What I did want was practical, hands-on ideas and advice I could get on with doing. That book is still my bible in many ways, although I have researched independently and put together a 'programme' that is suitable and tailored to my individual needs. Parts of the book were overwhelming and gave what would best be described as a flood of information. I have worked hard over the years to try to decipher the information best suited to myself. There is no instant method of doing that and it is very much a slow and time-consuming matter of trial and error to establish what works best. That is something I have found with Multiple Sclerosis. You cannot compare or contrast people with MS. I am different in my response and ability sometimes from hour to hour, never mind day to day. I scribbled notes and bit by bit I was piecing together a plan I would embark on immediately. There was food to buy, recipes to try, supplements to purchase and take, exercises to learn and do, numbers to phone, places to visit, lots to be ordered. I felt a sense of urgency, that there was no time to waste. I had to stay independent and able to manage day-to-day life for me and my family. I had to find a way forward. If there was anyone out there who could, it was most definitely me.

But first I had the arduous task to tell my immediate family the news. It was early afternoon when I contemplatively walked to my sister's house. She lived around the corner from me and worked from home at the time. On my reluctant arrival she gave me her usual enthusiastic welcome, immediately launching into chat as it was not out of the ordinary for me to drop by. I did interject early on as it didn't feel quite appropriate to continue with throw-away chitchat. I was unsure what to say and in the end, I told her straight that I had been diagnosed with Multiple Sclerosis. She was visibly disappointed and dejected, even though we all knew it was the main contender. She was, unlike herself, very quiet in her reaction. I found myself trying to convince her, or was it me, that everything would be all right. We arranged for her to come over later. We shared a very onwards and upwards attitude. We had our emotional outbursts, but MS would not be allowed to stand in the way of our lives.

She arrived later in the afternoon at my house to look after Elliot, while Allan and I went to tell my brother Ricky and his then wife. He was uncomfortably silent and his wife tearful. I told them I was already laden with ideas and information I had started to collect and that we all had to stay positive. They nodded in agreement with bitter resignation. By the time I arrived home I was emotionally drained as well as physically exhausted. We put Elliot to bed and settled down for the evening. I had made a brief telephone call prior to going out and told my best friend of some twenty-odd years. The doorbell rang and there she was. Alison was surprised to arrive to Elliot sound asleep as my husband, sister and I shared a bottle of wine as we continued to try and drink in the news. We told stories, laughed and drew strength in numbers that we were a team, a strong team. I was team leader and had already set about my tasks. Although it was still day one of this lifelong battle, I already had the beginnings of a plan of action drawn up. She commented that she had not expected to find us so upbeat and focussed. I had by then convinced myself it was not the end of my world. At least I knew what I was facing. After all, knowledge is power. My sister and friend left. I went to bed and although there was a silent tear, I was in Allan's arms and I knew I had all the support I was ever going to need. I was worn out by the last year and all it had flung my way. With it culminating in a diagnosis of Multiple Sclerosis I was going to need to be robust and count on my physical and mental stamina being strong enough to pull me through the months ahead. I had all the love and support you could ask for to bolster me. Elliot was in a contented sleep next door. It was going to be tough ahead, but let the battle commence. Having a couple of glasses of wine that night did not help with fatigue and my symptoms, but sadly it did help me cope and manage my emotional pain.

Telling my mum was much harder. The last thing any mum wants to hear is that her child is unwell or has a chronic condition. I had to pitch that one carefully. Allan and I drove to the seaside town of Largs, where she was visiting my aunt for the weekend. Initially they were delighted with their surprise visit. I explained that I had some news and the results of my MRI scan. My mum was devastated. I didn't get that one right. My mum has always said since I should have told her on her own, so she could have had some time to herself to take it all in. I could see the ache on her face. I did my best to be upbeat and reassuring, but Mum was a long way from that. She didn't say much, but she didn't have to.

When we drove home, I was by then pretty flat. I couldn't keep the positive 'it'll be all right' up. I needed some space to reflect and recharge. But in true Tricia style, the following day I suggested a trip to my dad's grave. It was January and freezing cold, but my sister took me to the empty graveyard where I spoke to my dad with some relief and poured out all my thoughts and fears. Sounds ridiculous probably, but he was the one person missing at the time. I had so much to say and we were all in need of his fighting spirit around. I took strength from my trip to his graveside.

After a short while I decided to visit my eldest brother Tony and tell him too. That decision was not an immediate one as relations were strained not so much with him, but with his wife. They would be the last people I would visit to tell in person. Those instincts that made me hesitate proved to be right. My sister and I made the journey to their house early on one evening mid-week. On arrival, we were given a reasonable greeting. My niece was happy at the surprise visit but seemed, unlike herself, a little insecure I had come to talk to her mum and dad. I shared a very close bond with her and reassured her everything would be fine. Little did I know that would be the last time I would ever see her. Her mum was to go on and ban the children from seeing me ever again!

I explained to my brother and his wife that I had come to include them and shared my news. That was

59

met with a silent reaction from my brother. His wife displayed little empathy and the conversation didn't go in a positive direction. Within seconds of announcing my news, his wife had bizarrely redirected the conversation to past events. That was indeed my strangest of reactions. I suddenly had no idea why I was there. Within days Tony's wife had made brief contact by telephone to inform me I was never to see my niece and nephews again. It was to all intents and purposes inexplicable. There is no contact now. There was the loss of the children, but that was not my decision. It took some time and I missed them dearly, but eventually you come to terms and move on. I still see my brother from time to time.

8

My Brush with Neurology

'We must accept finite disappointment, but never lose infinite hope.'

(Martin Luther King, Jnr)

One month after I found out my diagnosis unexpectedly, we arrived at the hospital for my next neurology appointment. It was another bitter cold day and it was the consultation with the neurologist that should have given me the results of all my tests. There is often an upside in life. I wasn't scared or overly nervous going to my appointment because I already knew my diagnosis.

I walked into the same waiting room as before. I was much more observant on that occasion as I was met with wheelchairs and walking aids all around. I hadn't noticed them in the same way previously. They seemed to be everywhere and filled the room. It became daunting all of a sudden. Other patients looked vulnerable and struggling. Or was it just that my perception had changed? My nerves began to take over and I had an overwhelming desire to leave. It was at that very moment I felt a strong surge of determination and courage. It ran right through my body. I pledged to myself there and then that I would work so hard and do everything in my power to steer my health and ability in a different direction. What was in front of me could not possibly become my future. I would not let it. I've always believed you can drive your own destiny and that was even more significant now.

That was my second consultation with the neurologist. He came across as reserved and pensive and it felt very much like he was there to do a job. It was all very matter of fact. He apologised again for how I found out I had MS. We moved on. You can't change the past, so there is no point going over it. I talked more and was almost enthusiastic about my future! I think in fact I was a little 'manic' and overwhelmed as I tried to cope with everything. I was so filled up with happiness being a mum, despite everything that was going on. It was such a juxtaposition of my emotions. The diagnosis of MS should have been devastating, but my memory doesn't tell me it was. As much as it hurt and frightened me, I just loved having my baby boy and all that came with it. It was almost impossible to give in to the feelings of worry and fear as having baby Elliot always served to lift my spirits. I had read a great deal, researched endlessly and already embarked on my ever-growing plan to tackle this disease, despite it being only one month since my diagnosis. In many ways there was relief I had a diagnosis, regardless of what it was, and I just wanted to move forward with our lives. We had put so much on hold. It felt like I had been treading water with regard to motherhood and raising Elliot. The time had doubtlessly arrived to change that.

The consultant briefly explained the medical approaches on offer to me at that time. None of which actually treated the disease itself. They consisted mainly of a group of drugs known as disease modifying drugs (DMDs). They worked by reducing the rate of relapses you may have and came with some pretty toxic side effects. They only 'might' reduce the number of relapses and no one knows if or when they are going to have one anyway! That didn't make a lot of sense to me. In reality I was being offered drugs with some pernicious side effects, but no one could predict if or when I actually needed them. Even then no one could say if the drugs would successfully stop any relapse. Those disease modifying drugs may also assist to slow down the progression of your MS. Again, that is neither definite nor measurable as it is unknown to each person what their progression of the disease will be. It was basically a gamble and I had to weigh up the odds. Other drugs that I might require could be prescribed by my GP as they relate to the different symptoms of MS. I would come across them as and when they were necessary in consultation with my doctor. I made the decision at that point in my journey to stick to my self-help guide and continue with my alternative approach. Just the thought of side effects was too much to bear. My body could take no more. I needed to repair it somehow, not inflict any more damage and distress. I had to look after baby Elliot, not have someone looking after me. I had no choice.

The consultant referred me for an appointment with the MS nurse and the physiotherapy department. Over the coming weeks I attended both and found them largely constructive, but certainly not inspiring or hopeful. The physiotherapy gave me practical exercises to tackle and I did so with my usual hard work and resilience. I had one follow-up appointment and expressed that the exercises helped me ever so slightly. That was my last appointment and they suggested I keep practising. Definitely helpful initially, but definitely short and sweet. The MS nurse was approachable and warm in her welcome. She listened more than she spoke and was very mellow in her manner. I found it a good place to air my worries, but there was not a great deal of response coming back at me. I felt I was surrounded by a real sense of acceptance of ill health. I recall that feeling clearly as the consultation was aimed more at how I should approach my life now I have a chronic disease. That is so far removed from how I think and live. I think the approach had more to do with the fact there wasn't an abundance of resources out there to support MS. I was learning that fast and the fact it was going to come down to me to be able to source alternative treatments and supports. I do recall one piece of advice from her that I have always used, which was simple, but effective. In those early days, I often wondered what could be the cause of unexpected tingles and sensations that would occur without warning. Over time you become familiar and more at ease with them. Initially they were a great source of alarm and tension. The nurse said that there are some days you will struggle to find explanation for and lack understanding of. She said rather than analyse and try to establish the cause, simply stop and rest. The nurse suggested doing something ordinary, but pleasant and restful followed by an early night. Rather than worry senselessly I have learned over the years to stop and take time out. Sleep is the best friend you can have with MS. It has never failed that in the morning I have felt better and, more often than not, the cause of my difficulty has gone for that time being. It may be a glass of wine or a cup of green tea and a rest. I have called on that advice on many occasions. I met the nurse once more and spoke by telephone. There seemed little else on offer. If I'm honest I couldn't wait to leave and go back to just being myself and not a 'patient with MS'. Least that's what it felt like. The whole hospital experience for me was shrouded in an air of acceptance and inevitability. It made me shiver on the one hand. It made me determined on the other.

The nurse had referred me to attend a newly diagnosed group. That took place in the evenings over six to eight weeks. I went along with Allan. It was a rather surreal experience. The room was full of almost panic-stricken people who had all just been diagnosed within the last two to three months with Multiple Sclerosis. The idea behind the group was sound, but on a practical basis it didn't meet our needs. People wanted to talk and ask questions about their situation rather than listen to generic advice. Understandably folk were a bit frantic and looking inwardly. I met a wide range of people, male and female, mostly between twenty-five to thirty-five years of age. I believe I was one of the oldest people there at thirty-nine years of age. The age range made it all the more difficult as it was a room full of such young people and all now with this burden for the rest of their lives.

Everyone had a different story to tell. The surprising fact being that, apart from myself, they were all taking the disease modifying drugs prescribed by their neurologist. It was more or less the case that the doctor prescribed it for them, so they dutifully took it. They had been diagnosed with a chronic condition; it simply followed they would receive medication. That was not me. What about a drug-free approach? It was worth considering in the absence of effective medicine being available. I believed I was in charge of my own body and had to find ways to make it work better. The drugs available at the time involved side effects for most people with no real proven improvement to their condition. That made little sense and offered me absolutely nothing. What struck me was people's reliance on their doctors and nurses and not on themselves. I was not prepared for someone else to be in control of my journey and to simply take a medicine because it was being prescribed to me. I talked openly to the others in the group about some of the things I had embarked on doing. They included removing butter and margarine from my diet. That was met with dismay and disapproval. One young woman, around about her late twenties, remarked that she couldn't imagine her toast without butter! My reply stayed in my head, but it was along the lines that I couldn't imagine my legs without walking! I met some decent people sharing in the same situation. I just happened not to think the same as many of them. That was not an unusual thing for me to experience!

I was referred for one more appointment to see a neuro-psychologist. It was all part of the newly diagnosed support offered at the Glasgow Southern General Hospital. She was a very lively and interesting doctor, precisely different from what I had encountered beforehand. Her enthusiastic greeting immediately lifted my spirits. The hospital investigations had been a truly lonely journey. I hadn't met or mixed with any like-minded people, patients or health workers. I completely rejected the call to surrender to being a sick person. Yes, I was having real physical difficulties, but I was a first-time mum with a bouncing, bright baby boy. I was starting a new chapter of my life, resolutely nowhere near accepting I was a person defined by a chronic disease. I told the doctor all the things I had researched and done with regards to adapting and making the necessary changes. That had particular emphasis on the ways I had found to care for baby Elliot. I almost had an air of excitement as I told her what I was managing to do and the ways I had discovered to do them. An example of that would be using the carry-cot part on Elliot's Bugaboo pram to move him safely from room to room when I was not confident to carry him myself. Sometimes just over to the changing mat. But hey, it worked and was not something to feel sad about. Once again I had found a way! I wheeled Elliot around our apartment in those early days in his pram. On some mornings, I would reconcile myself to time spent playing with Elliot on the double bed with lots of toys and books. I enjoyed all those times so very much that I would forget about my difficulties and restrictions. There was the odd occasion I would become frustrated because I could not manage to get to the kitchen to make and carry hot tea. I had to wait for my tea until someone arrived to visit. It was a little disheartening, but a lot worse things happen than having to wait for your cup of tea!

That doctor was thoroughly impressed and lifted my confidence a great deal. She further strengthened my resolve to keep on that track forward, not ever stopping for so much as a glance back. She explained that she had patients of many years with varying neurological conditions and the biggest obstacle they faced was not in fact their condition, but their inability to adapt to the necessary changes. She said I struck her with my willingness to make changes. The doctor said candidly that it would in fact make the difference in my future life no matter what it would throw at me. I have always remembered that consultation with great fondness and appreciation. It gave me a great big seal of approval to carry on with my tenacious attitude to find new ways to do old things.

I have continued to try to respond to each situation as it has arisen and adapt as required. I have learned that just about everything is all right to be done differently. You need to hold your head up high and do it your own way as long as you get there in the end. The doctor felt, on a very positive note, there was no need for me to return to see her and that I was far enough along the road to accepting I had to make change and not to try in vain to live my life as if it were pre-MS. That, I must note, is very different from accepting that having MS meant I would live a lesser life. I was both willing and able to make the necessary transitions. Having Elliot made it all possible. It still does to this day. Any time spent with him is so rich in love and joy that I am just Tricia, his mum. I see no obstacles and I hear of nothing that could hinder me.

To round off my neurological care with the NHS I was given one further appointment with the consultant neurologist. It consisted of a fairly brief update on matters and enquiry into whether I had reconsidered my position regarding taking the prescription drugs available. I told him I wanted to continue with what I was already doing and pursue my self-help journey. The consultant went on to explain the department was very busy and had a long waiting list. It would be my choice, of course, but I did not need to continue attending the neurology department. The option to be re-referred at a later stage of my disease would remain! I did not know what to say, which was unlike me, but I politely nodded. I was overwhelmed with rejection. I left the consultation room and subsequently the hospital somewhat dismayed. I collected Allan from the waiting room. He was smiling and eagerly waiting to hear how I had got on. I smiled back reassuringly and indicated to get on our way. We walked outside to the car park and I said sharply to Allan that I had been discharged. There was a real look of shock on his face. I explained to him what had just been put to me. He could not believe the news. We drove off with little more said, now in the knowledge that it was just us against whatever lay ahead. No more help was on offer at that time. Compromise wasn't on offer either. It was plain and simple that I should take their advice and medication or I should leave their services. Looking back, I have no doubt that the consultant did me the most enormous favour that day.

On our return home Elliot was happy with his Aunty Maggie, who was waiting intently to hear any news. I was to disappoint her, but brought her up to speed on what had happened. Without delay I returned to my self-help guide by Judy Graham. It was an absolute case of just getting on with it. I had my diagnosis and was discharged from neurological services. Everywhere you went in the house there were bits of paper, scribbled notes, ideas, websites, and phone numbers. My job was to try unravelling all of them and begin making the best plan possible.

9

Onwards and Upwards

*'Resilience is accepting your new reality, even if it's less good
than the one you had before.'*

(Elizabeth Edwards)

Those early days after diagnosis and hospital interventions
really came to light when I stumbled upon my 2007 pink
diary. I discovered they were a lot more difficult than I
remembered. On reading the diary, I unearthed how I
felt at the time and step-by-step details of my approach
to managing. I wrote an entry every day for the first
month. Fear and hope came through in equal measure.
The entries became sparser and like many things in life,
fell away. It gave me invaluable insight into the biggest
turning point of my life.

It seemed it was only over those first few intense
weeks I observed the need to write and record what I ate
and what I did. I was looking to see if there was a pattern
with anything I consumed and how it affected me. It was
all very early on and driven by an urgency to find some
answers. It was unlikely I was going to get any so soon
and from such a simplistic method. But I was desperate.
My diary entries didn't show up anything, but they did

record my frustrations. The predominant issue was that of tiredness to the point of weariness.

I recorded that I woke up every morning pondering what I could do on that day to help myself. I never had a day off. It seemed I had many tearful days and panic-stricken moments of how I was going to cope. I had more questions than answers. I was frightened and yet at the same time I displayed confidence I would find ways to get on top of this disease. I am not the type of person who shies away from any challenge, no matter its enormity. But it is only honest to share that it was clear from my diary entries I was scared at the same time.

I wrote a lot about Elliot being 'happy as long as he was getting my full attention'. That was obviously not always easy to give him, especially at the time, but I did my best. I went out more than I thought and seemed to do everything I could to keep busy. To my surprise, I carried on taking Elliot to parent and toddler groups as well as 'Bounce and Rhyme' sessions. I continued trying to live as normally as possible given the circumstances. In amongst everything that was going on I wrote about doing very ordinary things. They included going to the supermarket and soft play areas with Elliot. I described him as 'so amazing and wonderful'. It was very comforting to read those words and know that even in the most difficult of times I was still a happy mum and enjoying my beautiful baby Elliot.

One unexpected revelation from my diary entries was that I had returned to the doctor and been prescribed more Valium following my diagnosis. I had no memory of that and apparently used it later in the evening when

Elliot was tucked up in his cot for the night. I wrote that it helped when I was 'restless and couldn't sleep'. My diary records taking it on three occasions. It was obviously prescribed to help me through those initial weeks. It also tells me many years later that although I was out in the daytime carrying on as close to normal as possible, inside the pain and fear revealed itself when life quietened down of an evening.

I wrote a lot to describe the rather severe eye pain and discomfort I suffered. That led to me wearing sunglasses out and about in the east end of Glasgow in January and early February! Not a look that would fit in, but needs must! It helped mainly in shops with fluorescent lights.

Surprisingly I made entries in my diary over that first month suggesting Allan and I shared nights of lovemaking. That was certainly not something I had expected to read or be the case. Allan and I had always shared a healthy sex life, but that would not have been a time I would have considered it to have much place. Seems I was wrong and that despite how I was feeling, sharing closeness was another way to cope and strengthen our resolve together. Reflecting on it all these years later, I also believe it was a way of trying to remain the person I was before my diagnosis. It is extremely daunting when something can invade and start to take over your body and you are trying desperately to stop it. In fact, it is terrifying.

The unequivocal message from my diary was that I was absolutely resolute and committed to my self-help journey in the battle with Multiple Sclerosis. I had launched into it on the very day of my diagnosis when I purchased the self-help book by Judy Graham. I was embarking on a long journey. It would take me in many different directions and would last for the rest of my life. Everything I would try and all that I would do would be one piece of a very large jigsaw. That had been my vision literally within hours of my diagnosis. I still have no plans to stop searching. I will never rest thinking where I am is good enough. That means I am always living with hope and aspiration. I never know what I can achieve and what I can overcome until I try. Every piece of my MS jigsaw is significant and carries with it hope. Each one of them has been given my fullest attention and effort. That attitude means I am more in control of my own destiny. It is my life to live and I will work hard to keep living it as best as I possibly can.

Shock and feelings of helplessness accompanied me during all those initial MS attacks and subsequent symptoms. Once I had a lifelong diagnosis I had to find ways to support my body to recover somewhat and be pro-active to manage future symptoms. I would leave no stone unturned in my quest. I accepted almost immediately I would not be able to cure or rid myself of MS and all that comes with it. At the same time, I believed in myself and my unrelenting determination to be able to manage well enough to have a decent quality of life for me and my family. I still do.

The first thing I turned to even before my diagnosis was acupuncture. I came across it whilst doing a general search online. I was trying to source ideas that supported fatigue and trying to find an understanding of the ill health that had befallen me. I was gasping for energy so much of the time and on reading about acupuncture, it appealed to me. The belief is based on an ancient form of Chinese medicine, which suggests that an energy flows through our bodies, known as Qi (pronounced 'chi'). Where it is blocked in the body and cannot flow freely it is thought that illness and physical impairment can occur.[4] Acupuncture strives to improve the flow of Qi and is practised all over the world, playing a significant role in Chinese medicine. I made the decision to continue with this therapy after diagnosis as it had made a sizeable and positive contribution to my well-being. It was not something I could consider sustaining in the long run due to its financial implications, but it was early days and I needed all the support I could get.

On the morning after I found out my diagnosis of Multiple Sclerosis, I set off to my acupuncture appointment. It was pre-booked and serendipitously coincided with my news. It was by now my well-trusted friend and something I waited eagerly for every week. I always felt that with it I was trying to elicit some positive change in my health. As long as I was doing something, trying something, taking something, I had hope and kept pushing forward. It was more than a long shot that acupuncture could change the course of MS, but it always improved my energy levels, albeit temporarily, and it fed my soul. The therapist, Elaine Collins, put so much effort into me and my well-being. It was a refreshing change from my medical route. Even though the energy boost from each treatment was temporary, it was a big enough surge to go home to Elliot and have a small piece of quality

---

4 www.chineseacu.com: Chinese Acupuncture & Natural Therapy Center, Learning more about Qi and TCM

time with him. Playing with your baby is something most mums take for granted. As I made my way to the bus stop after each appointment, wobbly as I was, I did a little skip in my head most times in place of a physical one!

I was now constantly making changes and was what I refer to as being 'differently abled' to do most things. The mantra 'wecanfindaway.com' was never far away, nor the fact that we always did manage to. The most important issue in those early days was to continue addressing my debilitating fatigue so that I could look after Elliot. All part of that plan, more or less, was my next appointment!

I came across herbal medicine described as 'A powerful tool for healing'[5] in my research. It dates back thousands of years and is still widely used throughout the world today. I met with a wonderful, person-centred, holistic herbalist. An American woman named Erica Guthrie who always filled up my cup with compliments and confidence. Again, the approach incorporated all my needs, but with a focus on energy levels. My first appointment with Erica was made in Glasgow city centre. It was real fortune that led me to that herbalist. I chose her because of the convenient location from the bus stop and it would only mean a short walk for me! I immediately felt warmth towards Erica and connected with her. She actively listened whilst I did most of the talking on the first meeting. Erica prescribed my first herbal tincture mix to support my symptoms and hopefully increase my energy levels. I held a positive relationship with Erica and herbal medicine for some time.

---

5   www.botanical-medicine.org: The Medicine Garden: A Powerful Tool for Healing, JoAnn Sanchez

When Erica regrettably left to return home to the United States some eighteen months after that first meeting she gave me my notes and a history of my herbal medicine. I was genuinely surprised to read that I had described my situation at the first appointment as a possible 'new beginning'. That takes positivity to a whole new level indeed! I was thoroughly impressed with my absolute refusal to see Multiple Sclerosis as the big dark cloud it was so often characterised as. I was suffering a lot of headaches at that time and dizziness was a constant issue. But I refer to 'embracing the ups and coping with the downs as best I can'. I took my tincture religiously every morning without falter. Was it that? Was it my diet? Was it the acupuncture? Or was it just plain old me? I still don't know to this day what was helping and enabling me to do a little bit more day by day, but I do know each element was another piece of the jigsaw. I believe they all contributed. Unfortunately, after Erica left the United Kingdom I tried other herbalists and although they could prescribe similar tinctures, they in no way matched her knowledge and holistic vision. I left further appointments not feeling uplifted or even hopeful. There was the financial cost too. I could not maintain all the alternative therapies in the long run. I felt the herbal tincture had supported me to a point where I was doing better overall. The decision was taken to stop attending any herbalist in the absence of Erica and to ease financial pressures.

I was however firmly committed to continue taking my herbal supplements. From the first day of reading my self-help book and going to the health store to purchase the supplements, I was filled with hope. The list in the initial stages seemed endless. I had done some independent research and that added to the supplements recommended in the book. I endeavoured to work out by trial and error which ones helped and which did not. That was a slow and complicated process as well as costly. If it said anywhere it may help, had helped, kind of helped, hoped to help someone with MS then I got it and I took it! I set out a rather complicated plan of when I should take what and launched myself into it. To begin with I was taking thirty-one supplements a day! I rattled around for some time! I was spending more money each month on supplements than food. I never gave that a second thought as I was so focussed on trying to be an independent and able-bodied mum. I never had a day off from following my very strict supplement regime. I would wake up anticipating taking the next lot. Always holding out hope I might feel better. That feeling has never left me. Still I wake in the morning and look forward to getting downstairs to take my effervescent vitamin drink along with my supplements! I can say with some degree of confidence that they have made a significant difference to my well-being and ability. Elliot has benefited from all of that too and takes his supplements and vitamins daily. Allan hasn't escaped either! I have since adapted my supplement intake on meeting a Dr Gilhooly here in Glasgow. I will go on to explain the changes.

That was all costing money, and money we had not planned on spending. I may have been steadfastly determined on my self-help journey, but it came at a high financial price. We already had all the expenditure of a newborn baby, but hey, we had credit cards if we needed them. How do you decide a financial limit to help keep you walking and mobile? On the other hand, it is not realistic either to just spend limitless amounts. I felt the pressure those costs put you under. However, I was prepared to stretch it as far as I could. Even with the downside of all the money I was paying, I pushed on determinedly. People often say that you can't put a price on your health, but I have learned there is a price. And it's more than most people can afford. That is a difficult aspect for ordinary people. The NHS does its very best to provide free care, but it can be both limited and basic. That is mainly a result of its own financial limitations. If you are hoping to make bigger improvements with your health and attain a more acceptable quality of life, then you may need to think about additional and complementary treatments. We could pay for some of those. We had to make adjustments, difficult choices as well as compromises to accommodate that. We have little control over what happens to our health on many levels. Therefore, how you recover or manage any given illness should not be dependent on how deep your pockets are. But it can be. It may be more achievable to meet the costs of an acute illness for which there is a cure or that is a time-limited condition. However, with the diagnosis of a disease like MS, it is a lifelong condition. Therefore, any costs incurred are permanent. That is exceptionally difficult to sustain for most ordinary people. Multiple Sclerosis strikes people at a younger age and so there can be many years ahead where you need to pay for therapies and treatments. Added to that is the fact that more often than not the person loses their earning potential through the illness or it is at least reduced. That is a hefty combination to accept and live with.

What was on offer at no cost to me on the NHS was, if I'm kind, very limited and at best, if I'm honest, did not provide any positive aftercare which would lead to significant improvement in my ability. I was not in a position where I could accept my diagnosis of a debilitating and progressive disease to which I had to succumb. I had to be able to look after Elliot as well as possibly having a tiny desire to somehow still enjoy parts of life. The NHS felt very much a place and environment for people to be cared for whilst they were sick. I wanted to become well again, but I was able to acknowledge I had a chronic condition and that meant change. My aim was to manage it, but with aspirations for an improved level of ability and quality of life. None of that was on offer to me as part of the NHS and I had been discharged from the neurology department within weeks of my diagnosis. My new GP, Dr Lyndsay, was excellent, but there is only a limited amount a GP can do for MS beyond referrals and prescribing medication to alleviate basic symptoms. Most of those prescription medicines have a negative impact on my MS symptoms, in particular fatigue. In such circumstances, I am compelled to take a more natural and alternative route where possible. All GP referrals involve a long NHS waiting list. That requires time I do not have when I am struggling with my symptoms and need to be able and independent every day. So overall there seemed little treatment to improve my ability and health on the NHS. It also should be noted that at no point have I ever been offered long-term care from any department within the NHS for what is essentially a long-term condition. The NHS appeared to be stretched to breaking point. Treatments to improve my quality of life were therefore down to me. Just talking to someone outside the NHS who offers an alternative therapy or private medicine costs money, even before you find out if they can help or work with you. People are just trying to make a living and have some great skills and knowledge to share, but it's a tough learning curve when it's your own health and the potential difference between being able and not being able. I had to keep making choices to meet our financial capabilities. It was not easy. But it had to be done and still does for that matter.

There was one thing I could exert at least some control over in my journey and not at an obvious extra cost to begin with. That was my diet and eating habits. I came across a book that interested me and promptly ordered it. It was called *The Multiple Sclerosis Diet Book* by Dr Roy Swank. I was doing something new almost daily. The busier I was, the better I felt. On arrival of the book, I read it with gusto. I recorded information and took notes as necessary. Its message was clear. Eat a diet low in saturated fats and higher in unsaturated fats and oils. Our diet has evolved to be one that is higher in animal and saturated fats as well as including a high proportion of processed foods. That is unhealthy to everyone, but deemed to have a more profound effect on people with Multiple Sclerosis and other diseases. Good nutrition was the heart of that approach to managing MS. Simply put, it was 'basically a healthy diet'.[6]

6 *The Multiple Sclerosis Diet Book*: Introduction, x, Dr Roy Swank,
   Bantam Doubleday Dell Publishing Group, Revised Edition, 1998

I have adapted that diet, but still follow its basic principles. I prepare and cook all my meals using fresh ingredients. I eat a balanced and varied diet with an emphasis on getting plenty of protein. I start my day with a fresh vegetable juice. I try to concentrate on anti-inflammatory and green vegetables. My sister makes and delivers one every morning at 8.30 am faithfully. My diet is vegetarian and had been for twenty-five years before my diagnosis. Therefore, neither my protein or fat intake are from animal fats. The Swank Diet prescribes that you limit your consumption of saturated fats to less than 15 grams per day and ensure a minimum intake of between 20 and 50 grams of unsaturated fat or oils. I have become less rigid with counting the grams of fat as time has gone on and am more confident of the amounts and types of fats in the foods I eat. It must be taken into consideration when preparing each meal. I bake food rather than shallow fry where possible. I never deep fry or use oils high in saturated fats.

I reduced my dairy intake over the years in line with the Swank Diet advice. I listened to and watched how my body responded to the trial and error of those dietary changes. That has been my main way of determining what is best for me as an individual. I have become very much in tune with my body and continued with this method. Any slight alteration in the food I normally eat immediately impacts on my ability.

I have tried and tested other significant dietary advice in the world of MS. That has included going gluten free. I only tried for a few weeks initially as it was a very challenging diet on top of everything else at the time, including the demands of a young child and a husband with an exceptional work load. I have returned to a gluten free diet more recently since my husband became celiac and I have stuck with the diet for the longer term. I am cooking for both of us, so it is more manageable. I feel an improvement with my tiredness after meals and an overall improved sense of well-being. We live, learn and change all the time. Over the years, I became familiar with a pattern of lethargy after I had eaten most legumes and so I reduced my intake of them, noticing a sizeable improvement. I have since eliminated them from my diet altogether. Once again my method of trial and error, whilst taking note of the response from my body and my MS symptoms, proved most successful in informing what is best for me as an individual. My difficulty lies in that I am vegetarian, dairy free, legume free and eat a low saturated fat diet excluding processed foods and many cooking oils. I must get a balance between my dietary restrictions due to negative consequences and a healthy, varied and balanced diet. Not an easy task and I am not sure how much further I could trim my diet down and still get the calories and nutrients I need. I should add here that I enjoy my diet and there are many great meals I can make. I thoroughly enjoy eating a healthy diet and the only thing I miss is cheese!

Preparing and cooking food from scratch is not always quick. As time consuming as that has been, it has proved a very worthwhile focus. Elliot follows an exceptional diet as a by-product. I choose organic foods when I can and do not eat any processed foods where possible. There can be occasion when that does happen, but it is the exception and not the rule. It is on its own a very healthy way to live which is good for the whole family. It does mean not having many pre-cooked or convenience foods and that can be a tall order at times. It relies on always having the ingredients at hand as well as the inclination and energy to cook. Not to mention the time necessary. As that is difficult to maintain on a permanent basis I do keep a few tins of soup in the kitchen cupboard for those other occasions. Rare as they are. It is essential to be realistic and life means you don't always feel able to do things. Unexpected events can pop up at any given moment, but it goes very much against the norm when I do not eat fresh, organic foods. I try to cook in bulk and freeze dinners. Again, Allan is a great support, always preparing foods and vegetables to assist me. Overall it has been a positive contribution to all our lives. I will continue to do this for always. I avoid sugar except for natural sugar from fruit. This is all simply a healthier lifestyle no matter what and so we follow it in general at home. Although it should be said that both Allan and Elliot eat meat, it is mainly white meat and fresh fish. They most definitely don't avoid sugars although I try to manage Elliot's, at least, to a basic minimum. Allan indulges his sweet tooth from time to time.

It should be added that I am not someone who lives rigidly by this diet and never lapses. That would give a false impression. I have never been that sort of absolute and disciplined person in any walk of life. I follow it for the most part, but do stray from time to time. Be it that we are on holiday and the appropriate foods are not available or I don't have the time required or ability to cook that day. Or that after one of my more challenging days I fancy a glass of cava and a handful of crisps. On such an occasion, I will go ahead and have them. They will be baked of course! I even indulge from time to time in a weekend treat of take-away pizza. It must be from Pizza Express and made with good olive oil or rapeseed oil. It will have a healthy topping and no cheese! It is still rather scrumptious with that glass of cava! Life is for living after all and sometimes you need to live outside the box! It may not sound too adventurous. However, the consequences are not worth overdoing it. Therefore, I do it wisely. Hand cut and homemade oven-baked potato or polenta chips are another little luxury. It is not difficult to make great foods and indulge carefully here and there. Other times I just fall off the wagon and stay there for a short time. Then I think to myself, *it's time to get back on my journey again!*

The next big thing I had to confront was exercise. It had always played a big role throughout my life. That changed for the first time when my pregnancy became not so straightforward. I encountered some difficulties and only ever managed a few aqua-natal classes. That was about the extent of my exercise, and movement for that matter, over what amounted to two years. My body was weak and it had gone through the most colossal changes. I had to look at ways to strengthen it. That presented as problematic, if not impossible, at the beginning. I would even go as far as to say I was indeed frightened to try. My body was not strong and I no longer knew its capabilities.

Yoga would certainly not have been my first choice of exercise at any point up until then, but considering my diagnosis and how I was feeling it seemed an obvious thing to try because of its gentleness. I joined the class at my local sports centre and found it to be wonderful right from the beginning. The male instructor, Colin, was inspirational. He was non-judgemental and always pointed out the positives and could somehow find one in just about anything. On a cold, dull and rainy day he once started the class by reminding us that the sun was just above the clouds. 'Even though you cannot see it, it is still there waiting on us!' He could always help shift your perspective to a more optimistic one. His class was uplifting. The pace was very slow and the average age was sixty-something. Both suited me. All the fears I had to start with were unfounded and I had discovered something most suitable for the level at which I could perform. It opened my mind up to a different way of exercising and it should be said on a more spiritual level too. It worked for me, even though I hadn't expected it to. I found the physical stretching and positioning to be uplifting and energising. I felt almost immediate benefits to doing the yoga with my mobility not to mention my mental well-being. Very sadly indeed the instructor moved away and his replacement just never quite managed to take me to the places I went before!

The new instructor was much more concerned with her own performance and most definitely judged others. I even felt obliged to explain my unruly balance after a couple of weeks. I had never in all the previous classes with the former instructor felt that need. She, however, would look over and ask if I was all right. There was no need to. All it served to do was make me feel different. When I did tell her I had MS, because I felt obliged to, she brought me in a leaflet the following week. It had names and places of yoga classes specifically for people with MS. I was annoyed and disappointed at myself for telling her. The message was clear that I didn't belong in a 'normal' yoga class. The singular noticeable difference between myself and the other members of the class was my balance. It didn't warrant in any way exile to another group. I stared at the leaflet as I could barely bring myself to look up at her again. The strangest thing of all was that she hovered around expecting me to thank her. I nodded politely and moved away. That was the end of that then.

I've tried the odd yoga class since, but I have never come across one in which I settled again. I found the members of other classes to be of a younger breed. As they managed to turn their bodies inside out and stand on their heads I always felt completely inadequate! I missed my pensioner friends that my body and mind could relate to! I never told any other instructors and, because of that experience, I would feel awkward leaning on the wall or adapting the moves. I was without exception the slowest and last to complete each pose. I still have a real fondness of yoga and desire to practise. I do so as and when I have both the time and the right frame of mind. It was always something I had to allow myself some recovery time from afterwards. That makes it difficult to blend in with daily life. Therefore, it's not something I do as much as I would like to or enough to reap the real benefits. Since Elliot has gone to nursery and on to school, I have been engaged in going up and down on my daily bus journeys and that has left little time to practise yoga and recover sufficiently to make the next journey. It is something I will endeavour to pursue, particularly as Elliot grows older and more independent. Yoga is a positive tool when you have MS.

The other sport on my list to try was swimming. Swimming was never my thing and again I had to open my mind up to it. I don't do getting my hair wet! I'm not a fan of being cold, but I did not have a lot of choice. No longer able to do aerobic exercise from a standing position, I had to think of alternatives! For the first year or so I went to the local municipal pool. It was only a short bus ride away and therefore reasonably accessible. I had to walk across a car park to get to the complex itself, which was nearly always wet and blustery and meant I arrived somewhat fatigued to begin with. Although I often thought to myself that the wind acted as my 'camouflage' and diverted attention from my wayward balance and walking! The pool brought with it its own issues. It was very warm in the changing area and not the easiest access in and out of the pool. Those simple things were paramount. My slow swim would tire me out and I would have to get changed in the tiniest of spaces. I reacted to the heat on every single occasion. That meant by the time I finished I was wiped out. I often wondered if it was worth it. I only managed once a week usually. It was at least something, I would tell myself, and I was doing some cardiovascular exercise. Then again at the pace I swam, I'm not sure if it would count as that!

The time came when I decided to up my aerobic exercise and do it with more consistency, as well as somewhere the environment was better suited to my needs. I joined a private gym with a swimming pool and found things improved. Not everything was perfect and there will always be challenges attached to doing exercise for me. However, the environment was more acceptable. I had to endure the additional costs, but I have never felt there was any choice because I must keep my muscle strength and stamina at an acceptable level. It is imperative to my mobility. On the positive side, I had no more reactions to the heat. There was easy access into the pool and I even managed some weight resistance training too. I squeezed in some uplifting yoga poses when stretching and warming up before using the gymnasium. I attempt to go every week as long as life does not get in the way! I feel the benefits when I do and notice the difference when I don't. It is a lifelong commitment for me and I will always keep going back, even if I do happen to miss a couple of weeks from time to time.

The diet, the supplements and exercise are all vital pieces of the MS jigsaw in my bold self-help plan. I am committed to each one. The complementary therapies, although they offered valuable support at different points in my journey, were not financially sustainable on a permanent basis. I continued with an open mind, willing to take on board new information and try any procedures and treatments as and when I came across them. It really was a case of onwards and upwards.

10

Reaching Out

'If you accept the expectations of others, especially negative ones, then you will never change the outcome.'

(Michael Jordan)

I kept on looking and searching for another piece of the jigsaw day by day. Where else, I thought, would be better than the MS Society itself? I viewed their website and read as much as I could possibly take in. I ordered several of their information leaflets, which were sent to me by post. There was a great deal of information and it was not an easy task making sense of it all, but I was hopeful that it could help me. The information was very factual as you would expect but, for me, it lacked emotion. I did learn and assimilate many facts about MS. It seemed to me the MS Society was there to give you information and help you learn to live with MS. I know it works for lots of people and meets their needs; however, I was looking for something very different at the time. I wanted inspiration and I had aspirations. I was not prepared to settle into a life living with a chronic disease. I am still not. I was and always will be looking to overcome any obstacles and find out what I can do to be more able, as opposed to accepting and living with not being able. There is no doubting the value and service the MS Society provides, but its initial information and messages were not resonating with me.

Surprisingly and through absolute curiosity I did sign up and subscribe to their monthly magazine. It was in the very early days and I thought it was imperative to keep abreast and informed of everything going on in the world of MS. I have always believed that just one tiny piece of information found somewhere could help me. I was not going to cut off any avenues available to me. I remember vividly when the post would arrive with my copy of the MS monthly magazine. Almost without exception I would read it at my kitchen table whilst Elliot played on his mat in the living room, just through the door. I was always disappointed. The stories told were of the difficult and grim times associated with Multiple Sclerosis. It was always scary and seldom offered me much reassurance. It seemed more a case of assuring you what was going to happen. I was not comfortable with that. If I'm honest, I felt there was a lack of hope. The focus always seemed to be of hardship and how much help people needed. The pictures were of people using walking aids and requiring assistance. It is paramount to point out that I recognise MS does affect people in those ways, all at different stages of their journey. It is therefore important to respond and support them. But it became clearer to me with every magazine that came through my door that it was only serving to panic me as someone newly diagnosed. It was hard to stay positive and enjoy life with my baby whilst surrounded by pictures of mobility aids, people in wheelchairs, vulnerability, financial hardship and suffering. *Surely there must be an alternative route*, I would think to myself. One that focussed more on what you could do than what you couldn't. It was not that I didn't recognise there was hardship, but in my life it was not going to be the focus. I was not willing to accept my future would be filled in that way.

There were articles that told stories of someone or something that may inspire, but it would be fair to say they were few and far between. I always remember every page you turned over between stories was full of adverts. Those adverts were all for mobility aids and scooters. I know the MS Society has to make its money to fund itself from somewhere. I do remember thinking about that way back in those early days. I deliberated the point that only people who didn't have MS would fill the magazine with those pessimistic adverts. It felt like they were spreading a miserable outlook about the future. You were simply expected to accept it. I recall that the people in those adverts were always smiling, as was the person aiding them. That was certainly not how I saw it and a brand-new, shiny mobility scooter arriving at my door would certainly not have put a smile on my face at that time. It was most certainly not a magazine for the newly diagnosed. How could you possibly read that and feel any hope or positivity about your future? I always felt it was about being sick and needing help. Whereas I saw myself as someone who undoubtedly needed to look after myself and have measured support, but I was also someone who could and would go on to do and achieve. I was a new mum with both our futures in front of me. I cancelled my subscription. We wanted different things.

I feel duty-bound to add that I respect the role of the MS Society and it has an important part in many people's lives. It was simply not conducive to my ambitious and active outlook. Multiple Sclerosis is undoubtedly difficult, but so can life be itself. My choice is not to focus on those difficulties, but to focus on what I can do, achieve and how I can help make a positive difference to my MS. I think the MS Society would do well to broaden its perspective and try to include a wide range of people and stand points. The whole thing made me feel there was an air of inevitability about my future and I completely rejected that. I still do. Whatever the future holds I want to live my life reaching upwards all the time. I felt that communications from the MS Society were interfering with that. No one in this world would be comfortable with a vision of their end game through ill health. I was no different.

The next place I reached out to was an organisation called Revive. It was based in Glasgow to support people with MS and offered complementary therapies at no cost. I made contact and arranged an introductory appointment. As I arrived I was feeling nervous and unsure what to expect. My appointment was booked for the same afternoon they held their support group for people with what appeared more progressive MS. I had no prior knowledge of that fact as I entered the premises. That meant I walked into a row of wheelchairs and support chairs. The people in the group displayed the effects of MS to varying degrees. It was maybe not the best idea to have newly diagnosed people in at the same time? Or they could have given some advice to prepare people? Regardless, it was what it was on that day.

One worker said hello to me. The other workers continued in their attempts to entertain the people all lined in a row in their wheelchairs and mobility scooters. At least that is how it came across to me. All I could see were cans of fizzy juice and snack foods. That image has always stayed with me. There I was searching for the best diet to support myself in my journey with MS. I tried not to be judgemental and I most certainly was not criticising any of the people with MS. I just felt maybe the Revive service could have tried to do a little better by them? But I did not know any other background to the group members or the service and so it was better to hold still my first impressions.

I was restless and somewhat agitated as I waited. I was feeling overwhelmed at being met with the group of folks who had more progressive MS as I was not prepared for that. I had only been recently diagnosed, I had a young baby and my head was in turmoil. I was living in constant fear. I had the terrifying feeling I was looking at what lay ahead for me, and getting my head around that, sitting alone with no support, was a truly awful experience. In those early stages, everything was filled with panic and I was still unsure how I would manage my MS. My thoughts turned to leaving, but that was not my usual style. I sat on the end seat of the L-shaped row. No one brought me into the conversation in which the workers came across as rather loud and the participants seemed to have to fight to get a word in. I waited until I was called by the nurse.

I remember her office to be dark. I sat down on the very plain seat of the chair with nothing around me to lean on or hide behind. The nurse explained about the services and the therapies they offered at no cost. One of them happened to be reflexology, which was on my list as a piece of the jigsaw I planned to try. I thought to myself at that point, there had been a reason I stayed on. I could try reflexology at no personal cost. Considering the financial outlay I had committed to since my diagnosis, that factor itself was a very attractive one. The rather distant nurse went on to ask me about my symptoms and how I felt. I hadn't spoken to many people outside my family about having MS and even that was limited. It felt a step too far, as it was only a short while after my diagnosis. I did however try to open up. Big mistake, opening up to a virtual stranger. You leave yourself wide open and completely vulnerable. I told her all my thoughts and feelings about raising Elliot and my trepidation as to how I would cope as a mum. I managed to squeeze out my greatest fear that I wouldn't be able to run around after him as he grew to a toddler and beyond. Her almost callous reply will stay with me forever, 'and you never will'. She said it as part of a sentence in relation to my abilities, but those were the words that rang in my ears. That marked the beginning of the end of my Revive experience.

I regrettably did try the reflexology. The treatment was in line with the rest of my experience. It was cold, emotionally as well as literally, and very impersonal. I felt like an inconvenience. The reluctant therapist used minimal communication. She commenced the treatment and I had no idea what she was doing or why. She chose not to tell me and I lay there feeling like an object. I could not get out quick enough as I cried my way walking from side to side to the bus stop. I was very vulnerable in those early days. So much was unknown and I was not strong enough yet to shield myself from unwelcome and unnecessary harm. With hindsight and confidence many years down the line, I would not have completed the treatment. I would have called a halt to it sooner rather than later and assertively told her why. We deserve to be treated as equals and with respect at all times, under all circumstances.

I returned home to Elliot, being looked after by my mum. Her eyes filled expectantly with hope as she asked how it had gone. It was very difficult for my mum to have her daughter deliver her a beloved grandson and then watch her demise under the power of Multiple Sclerosis. She saw me vulnerable and shaken that day. I reckon I get my strength from her. She gives new depth to the term 'Keep calm and carry on'.[7] And so we did just that. Revive was the first piece of the jigsaw I discarded. No help at all at that time.

Still unwilling to settle and accept my pessimistic prognosis, I pushed on day by day. But I learned that reaching out, almost in a state of panic, was not the way forward. I decided to focus on the positive measures and actions I had already taken and that were delivering good results.

---

7 www.keepcalmandcarryon.com/history

11

Early Retirement

'I can't change the direction of the wind, but I can adjust my sails to always reach my destination.'

(Jimmy Dean)

I had to think early on in my self-help journey about how I was going to cope with my employment and working life. I was on what seemed like a mission to improve my well-being and ability. Despite everything I was doing and taking, my symptoms were such that a return to the classroom looked an extremely unlikely option. My job demanded a high level of physical mobility compared to my previous posts in mainstream education. I had been away from mainstream for around five years and hadn't missed it for a day. Even if a return there was indeed possible, my other symptoms would have prevented it from becoming a reality. There was a big decision facing me and I had to find out more information before I could make it, as well as ascertain how my employer would react.

I contacted the EIS (Educational Institute of Scotland) Union. The representative had very little knowledge of what options were ahead of me. I recall a rather depressing telephone call where he tried to assure me there were teachers supported in their classrooms and positions who were in wheelchairs! I was standing in my garden in the sunshine watching Elliot, who was barely one year old, playing on the grass as I spoke to him. I was newly diagnosed and that was his first port of call. It certainly was not mine and served to lower the tone of my day as well as panic me. We need to learn to think before we speak. Maybe collect some information and facts? Some sources suggest only a small number of people with MS will go on to use a wheelchair on a regular basis and that is only after many years of having the disease.[8] I had only been diagnosed for a couple of months and talk of being in a wheelchair served to do nothing but alarm me. I'm sure he continued with his day as normal after our conversation, but I certainly didn't. I was down, distraught and even more concerned about my future.

It was not long before I went for a very thorough medical at my employer's request. It was at that point I realised the extent of the loss of feeling my feet had suffered. The education department arranged a consultation with a doctor to determine if I was in fact fit and able to return to work. That was standard procedure following a prolonged period of absence. It was held at an office block in the city centre. As I sat down in the bland, whitewashed room with its metal chairs and medical equipment, I was agitated. The whole situation felt unreal as I was very routinely examined in an almost business-like manner. I knew that a return to work for me was out

8   www.mstrust.org.uk: Understanding MS, Facts and myths about MS

of the question, but the outcome of the assessment would conclude whether or not I received early retirement and the benefits that came with it. During the physical examination, the doctor asked me to respond when I could feel anything on my legs. He used a large, pointed metal instrument. It was much like an extended needle. I didn't respond very many times. When I sat up at the end of the examination the doctor showed me the cold-looking, sharp utensil. I had no idea that he was prodding my feet and legs with such an implement. It was only then I realised just how little feeling I had in my feet and at the bottom of my legs.

That very formal medical examination was followed by an interview with my manager. The decision was taken that I would not return to my teaching post. I never considered I would again. It was not the worst decision or most difficult to accept of my MS journey. I had taught for over fifteen years across a range of educational establishments and teaching had taken me to different destinations. As much as I had loved it, it had also taken its toll.

I was retired from teaching and my pension would serve to support us a little financially. That would be a good bit less than my salary, but it was positive to have some long-term and consistent support in those difficult circumstances at least.

My place and position in life were now dominated by motherhood and Multiple Sclerosis. There was no room for anything else. The timing was not planned and my teaching career did come to an abrupt end. But there was no great loss. I had enjoyed a very full career over my years in education. It had taken me on my travels, given me a wealth of opportunities and an inspiring blend of life experiences. I had met some wonderful kids and relished the thoroughly fulfilling times I was privileged enough to share in their learning and development. I had been truly blessed with my career. On the other hand, there were always challenges adapting my teaching practice as I moved from place to place. That made my exit easier and brought with it some relief.

It was time to concentrate on myself and my immediate family. I was very focussed on my self-help journey. Elliot filled up my cup every day and I had a lot going on. It was not hard therefore to accept the ending of my teaching career, even though I was not quite forty years old.

12

Dr Gilhooly

'If it were not for hopes, the heart would break.'

(Thomas Fuller)

A year had passed since my diagnosis. I was slowly and reluctantly finding ways to live with MS. I was retired from teaching and my self-help journey was well underway. I was always open to anything that could come along and possibly help or support me. I was doing reasonably well managing to look after Elliot, but I was fully aware I had quite some way to improve before I would be able to cope with him growing into a pre-schooler and beyond. Remember, I was on my medical journey alone with only my self-help book and Google search engine to guide me. Elliot had just turned two and even though I knew I still had the luxury of the pram for a while yet, I appreciated it was time-limited. It was springtime 2008 when I came across three different sources who all mentioned the same doctor in Glasgow who specialised in Multiple Sclerosis. His name was Dr Tom Gilhooly. I decided to arrange a consultation and waited enthusiastically for my appointment, pondering if it could be an important part of the jigsaw. More than that, I was hoping at last I would not be alone in the medical world with my disease anymore.

The clinic was on the south side of the city and its location necessitated a car journey. It was situated at the edge of an old shopping centre car park and you were always exposed to the elements, which were rarely kind! The clinic was new and well appointed, much in contrast to its location. It was my first experience of private healthcare and although I was nervous, I also had a great big bag of hope with me. Immediately on meeting Dr Gilhooly I felt a rapport. He had the same holistic approach as I had and a thirst to find new treatments to support people with MS. He was very down to earth and I left that first consultation with my cup filled with a different kind of hope and the feeling that I was no longer just relying on myself and my self-help book. Dr Gilhooly paid great attention to the fact that managing Multiple Sclerosis was not a matter of doing one thing or taking one medicine. He was perfectly clear that although each thing contributed, they were part of an overall package. That fitted exactly with my idea of everything being part of a big jigsaw. At long last I connected with someone and their optimistic, uplifting attitude to Multiple Sclerosis. From the moment I entered his consultation room, it was about what can be done. A new journey had begun to discover more ways to improve my quality of life.

At last I had direction with my supplements and dropped from taking thirty-one a day to two combined supplements! The new supplements were a specially formed combination for people with Multiple Sclerosis called Baseline AM and PM. They incorporated much of what I was already taking. I was very grateful to have guidance in that area at last. It simplified my routine and brought with it an initial reduction in cost. I adapted my diet to include a high Omega 3 intake, taking additional supplements. Dr Gilhooly explained research over the years had discovered many health benefits of Omega 3, the most important being its anti-inflammatory properties. Omega 3 became integral to my diet and I made the move to become completely dairy free. I kept with the other main principles of the Swank Diet. The decision to start taking high-dose Omega 3 supplements, which are fish oils, was a difficult one for a vegetarian as I am. I was assured it would make a real difference. I certainly needed a difference in my life, so the choice was made for me. It was not a decision I reached easily, but I had to put my health and ability first.

At the next consultation six months later (October 2008) Dr Gilhooly introduced a new drug into my care. That drug was called low dose naltrexone, often referred to as LDN. It is what is known as an off-label or unlicensed drug, occasionally used by doctors. LDN is a small amount of the previously licensed drug naltrexone. It was discovered that when given in low doses the drug temporarily blocks the opioid receptors in our brain. It is during that time the LDN stimulates the production of our body's own endorphins,[9] thus helping to modify and restore the immune system. I am very clear that it is not a 'wonder' drug as it was sometimes portrayed. It does not offer any cure, but simply supports the individual's own immune system. It is however cheap and many thousands

---

9   www.lowdosenaltrexone.org: What is low dose naltrexone and
     why is it so important?

of people have found it to be effective in treating a variety of diseases. I was about to become one of those people.

During the weeks and months that followed I had to work hard and dig deep. The dosage of LDN was altered for a period of trial and error to get it correct. It took a good few months and there were days when I felt worse than I did before I started taking it. But I stuck with it as I trusted Dr Gilhooly and had done extensive research on LDN myself. That was the point where many may have thrown the towel in, but something told me to keep going. That was probably one of the most difficult times since it all began. Long winter days at home with Elliot who was only two and a half and not one for contentedly watching CBeebies on television! Responding to the needs of a very active and energetic toddler was extremely challenging and taxing, but my mum was around to help a lot during those days. The weather combined with fatigue and my physical symptoms made the rest of the year very difficult. We stuck together as a close family, looked after Elliot and literally just got by. Life was not addressed as it would be normally. We just had to scrape by doing the bare minimum. Times were tough, but luckily so were we.

In the new year, the LDN began to show positive results and I settled on a dose of 2.5 mg. That worked best for me. I was sensitive to LDN and slight changes in dosage seemed to affect me. I had tried and tested it at higher doses, but to my displeasure. The dietary changes were well under way. Overall and at last there were improvements in some of my symptoms. The impact of taking a high level of Omega 3 was also beginning to show. I had more energy and my walking was better some of the time. My legs were, let's say, more co-operative. Without a shadow of doubt the biggest improvement was my fatigue. Combined with my exercise routine it all amounted to increased stamina and strength. That was not on every day, but on more days than before. I felt as good as I had done since my diagnosis. Certainly well enough to cope better with Elliot at home on a day-to-day basis.

I felt so strongly about the importance and value of LDN I joined up to support a campaign to raise awareness. I was experiencing the benefits and desperately wanted to share the good news. LDN is inexpensive and so does not have the interest or backing of pharmaceutical companies as it would not render enough profitability. No one is prepared to bankroll clinical trials as a result. I roped in others from my family and we set up our stall in Glasgow city centre. We took folding chairs and a small table along with a huge bundle of leaflets. My sister threw in a tin of chocolates to tempt people over! I met with other people from Glasgow's LDN community and spent the afternoon trying to share information about this rather special and little-known drug. If one person from that day discovered LDN, it was worth it. We were gathering signatures for a UK-wide petition. The significance of LDN made its way after that to the UK Parliament in the shape of a working party. So watch this space, maybe one day it will become available on the NHS and lots of people could benefit from it.

Allan and I attended the first European Low Dose Naltrexone Conference held in Glasgow in the spring of 2009. We learned a lot and the testimonials were overwhelming. It was claimed that LDN can help people who have other diseases, including some cancers and arthritic conditions. The research and reports from around the world told of an unfolding story, which could help change the lives of many people. It had already done so. Being inexpensive with no side effects, it seemed unthinkable not to afford others the opportunity to access LDN. I knew it was something special and I had been fortunate enough to get the chance to take it. I wanted others to share that opportunity.

After one year of my new dietary changes and Omega 3 intake I was tested to identify my balance of Omega 3 and Omega 6. I had taken steps to reduce the amount of Omega 6 I consumed and at the same time introduced Omega 3. A good balance between them is very important for optimum health. The test results showed I had 63% Omega 3 to 37% Omega 6. Overall a healthy balance and my lifelong task was to maintain that! Things were certainly moving in the right direction.

My timing in meeting Dr Gilhooly and getting some medical support was very important indeed. I had taken myself as far as I could on my own and needed some professional guidance. I was faced with the unnerving prospect of Elliot growing out of his pram and significantly losing that support with my walking. It seemed possible that some of my interaction and direction from Dr Gilhooly may hold the key on how to move forward. There had been a convincing and favourable improvement in my health and ability since I had gone under his care. I continued to have consultations with him over several years. They changed the direction of my MS journey. That was always for the better. We focussed on different things and each and every time I met with him he had something new to bring to me. His sheer commitment and enthusiasm in the battle against Multiple Sclerosis knew no end. He was driven to help people like me. I am very grateful that I found Dr Gilhooly on my journey.

13

Complementary Care

'When we are no longer able to change a situation, we are challenged to change ourselves.'

(Viktor E. Frankl)

I thought it would be a good time to contact the homeopathic world. With the positive outcomes from Dr Gilhooly's care, I wanted to add what I could into the equation to sustain my ability. I had held an interest since coming across Dr Leckridge in my newly diagnosed group. Following a discussion with my GP she referred me to the homeopathic hospital. There are various additional therapies and supports out there that can complement general medicine. A factor not always considered by some in the medical world, but a viable option nonetheless. They can make a positive contribution to a great many people in their struggle with disease and ill health. I had found up until then great support and benefit from some of those and eagerly anticipated my relationship with homeopathy. Glasgow hosts a Centre for Integrative Care, which offers a range of complementary therapies and homeopathic remedies. The overall purpose is to improve patient well-being and increase the resilience of patients with largely incurable, long-term chronic conditions. There are limited NHS resources to help improve a patient's health so this is an invaluable service the NHS provides.

It took some months before I got my first appointment. It was with the same Dr Leckridge I had previously come across. My mum watched Elliot that day and subsequent days I attended. It was quite a travel from my house, but I am someone who always tries to rise to the occasion. It was challenging, but curiously inspirational too involving both the bus and train. I hadn't been travelling much or independently for quite some time, so I chose to stop off for a decaf cappuccino with soya milk. I rarely got the chance to do ordinary, everyday things anymore. It was nice to feel 'normal' once in a while, even though that's not something I've made much acquaintance with throughout my life! No matter how difficult the journey was, I always felt a great satisfaction and sense of winning against this disease when I triumphed over anything. It was not a journey I would relish in the winter, but we would cross that bridge when we came to it. My walking and balance were good enough to get me where I was going. That may have been a debatable point, but when you are as determined as I was they did the job! As time progressed I came to rely more on a car journey to get me there. Whether the independent travelling lost its initial appeal or my legs got too tired, I am not sure. I think it was more likely because I learned to stop pushing myself so much.

My first appointment was comfortably long so I could talk in as much detail as necessary without feeling rushed.

That was somewhat of a novelty when dealing with the NHS or whenever no money was changing hands. I was very relaxed almost to the point of enjoying talking and being able to express my feelings and fears. Dr Leckridge had a very special and individual style with his patients. He was clearly exceptionally knowledgeable and came across with immense integrity. I remember asking him why he had moved into homeopathic medicine after thirteen years as a GP. He said that he was 'tired of simply stopping people being sick' and instead wanted to 'try and make people better'. At the end of the consultation I was given my first prescription for a homeopathic remedy.

Not everyone can be keen on homeopathy and there is a lot of scepticism around it. That will remain and I would go as far as to say I have had GPs frown on the idea. It is sometimes claimed that any success is a result of the placebo effect.[10] That is something I have come across more than once on my journey. I think as a patient I need to be listened to and given more respect. Medical science has been able to offer me very little so far to improve my quality of life, yet it often stands to rubbish anything else that does. I would suggest people try to be more open-minded. When the neurological services are limited in what treatments they can offer, it would be a good idea to support people to look elsewhere and respect services that do support people through long-term conditions. When someone is diagnosed with a chronic condition they are often forgotten about in many ways. They are expected to go off by themselves and just cope independently. I

---

10 www.sciencebasedmedicine.org: Overview of Homeopathy

think we are much better in the UK at addressing acute illnesses and ailments that arise. Not everyone has the good support I am privileged to have. That makes it very difficult for many people. Providing better services and assistance is paramount to individuals having any quality of life. The Centre for Integrative Care provides support over the long term and is an essential element in many people's lives. I have since returned on numerous occasions and it has played an important role in my MS journey over the years. The holistic care was invaluable and I felt improvement in both my physical and mental health after attending for a prolonged period.

We need to move away from the culture where we search for a pill to cure a disease. For so many people, that does not exist. It feels unacceptable to reject many of the alternative and complementary care models under the umbrella that they offer false hope. It is in fact plain and simple hope we all need and desire. The fact it regularly renders effective is a clear bonus. I want to be the one to judge what is good for me or good to try. I am not 'sick and vulnerable' as often claimed by the media when they are trying to run down alternative and pioneering treatments. That is particularly true when there is a cost attached. I am confident and assertive and very able to judge for myself. All the complementary care professionals and private doctors I have met have been of the utmost integrity and professionalism. They dedicate their working lives to trying to give people like me a quality of life as opposed to no quality, which is currently on offer. Other professionals need to stop criticising and knocking them down. Those people put their professional reputation on the line. Without them I shudder to think what my life would be like. I certainly would not be writing this book or be the mother I am to Elliot. Conventional and complementary medicines need to work together to support people with conditions such as mine. It does not have to be one or the other.

The way I have always seen life is that if you cannot offer an alternative, then allow others to present their ideas. Let them go forward to try and elicit positive outcomes and do not criticise what they are trying to do. I try to achieve more than most every day. That is made possible by my alternative and complementary care as well as private medical care. I am capable of making informed choices as to whether I should use those services or indeed pay for them where necessary.

14

Elliot Starts Nursery

'I know there is no straight road No straight road in this world Only a giant labyrinth of intersecting crossroads.'
(Federico Garcia Lorca)

I was very grateful I had both conventional and complementary medical support, as my next big test was coming. I had made improvements since that medical care had been introduced and could look after Elliot with more ease. It may not seem like much, but when you have come from a starting position like mine, it was a noticeable difference.

Elliot had turned three and was due to start nursery school in August 2009. Allan still worked at the university, which meant every day I would take Elliot to and from nursery on the bus. I would have to walk up and down a hill to get to the nursery itself. That probably sounds straightforward to most people, but I would have to rely on being physically able every day. That was not going to be without complication. It was time to let go of my red Bugaboo pram. We had a buggy to be kept for occasional use, but otherwise I was letting go of my trusted friend and literally what I leaned on. That new journey was to start in earnest mid-August. It was a big transition for both Elliot and me. He was a very content toddler at home. We spent a lot of one-on-one time together. With Gran as a regular visitor, it all added up to a comfortable home life. He would be left much more to his own devices at nursery. It was a lot to deal with, but it is for most children. The difference being that I think it was a particularly poor nursery. I was unable to get Elliot a place at the other local nursery, even though I did try, and struggling myself to travel further afield. I was stuck with it or no nursery place at all.

I had to deal with many changes once Elliot started nursery. That presented a host of difficulties as I had established routines and set up ways of coping, particularly on the more difficult days. My worst-case scenario up until that point was that if I had to just get through the day I could do so by going from room to room in my house. I only had to contend with amusing Elliot and that could be done in the one room when circumstance required. I would no longer have the security of being able to choose to stay at home. It was now going to be a matter of getting up, getting ready and heading down to the bus stop for the first leg of the journey. That would be my routine five days a week regardless of my well-being. There would be no choice anymore. If my legs weren't working well that day, it was just tough luck. It still had to be done. If my balance was poor, it was the same thing. It still had to be done. There was to be no respite when fatigue raised its ugly head. On the days, up until then, when I felt any of those things happening or I just couldn't keep going, I had been able to stop. That was no longer going to be the case. I can trace back to some of those days and it was very hard going indeed. We glibly say at times that 'we just need to keep going' and 'there's nothing else for it'. That reality for many is a hard one. I've often wondered what would happen if my legs refused to go any further. I have felt very close on occasion. That is why I have worked so hard on all the things I do and take to manage my MS. It has been to enable me to cope with the simple things like getting Elliot to nursery of a morning. Even though I had all those fears and the apprehension that came with them, Elliot started nursery and so the changes were inevitable.

I was not in charge of my day anymore. I would maybe decide to do some domestic chore when I returned home from dropping Elliot off. That would more than likely render me not fit enough for the next part of the day. I may have done some written work, which would in turn put my balance off. It would also challenge me cognitively and always caused a stretch of fatigue. No matter what I chose to do, there would always be a consequence for me. That is still the case. I have got used to making choices each day and built up my stamina to manage. I have found coping strategies and rely on my dogged persistence to push on and do what must be done.

The biggest influencing factor was the effect of the daily travelling on me. That had many lingering consequences and was mostly because of having to walk up and down the small hill four times each day. If Elliot's nursery had been situated on flat ground, so much would have been different. But it wasn't and I just had to get on with it as best I could. At the very start of my journeys I could be anonymous as I didn't know anyone and tended to keep myself to myself. It didn't seem to matter if I walked straight or if I staggered from side to side. Elliot was small and walked with me, so I managed on most days. I must say I took a lot of deep breaths and was always very relieved to shut the front door on my return home.

Even with Elliot at nursery for some time, let's just say he wasn't too keen. That was never to change. I could clearly see why, but I thought it was important he socialised with other children so I continued to take him. It was not an easy decision to make. I could have made life a lot less troublesome by taking Elliot out of nursery. I would not have had the bus travel or the hill walk. I had to collect him after merely two hours so I was usually only back in the house for a short while. It was a taxing morning and it was every morning at that. He wasn't learning much from what I could see. I am still not sure if it was the right decision.

As Elliot moved on to his second year of nursery, I was more and more relying on my legs to be strong and my fatigue to be under control. It was tough at times and on many days, I struggled. Elliot was also invited to party after party at soft play centres. That involved a great deal of stamina and strength. My walking and balance were continually under scrutiny and being tested. Elliot was four and we had parted company with the pram. It was November (2010) of his second year at nursery and it would be fair to say I needed a little bit of help. I had my six-month scheduled appointment with Dr Gilhooly at the clinic.

15

CCSVI Procedure

'Life is inherently risky. There is only one big risk you should avoid at all costs, and that is the risk of doing nothing.'

(Denis Waitley)

It was a cold and miserable November evening when I arrived for my appointment with Dr Gilhooly. The dark nights had arrived and with them the winter weather. That made my travels tougher and my walking more unruly. I was cold and shivery when I got inside the clinic and had a good while to wait, but it gave me a chance to compose myself. I still managed to lose my balance a little as I walked into the consultancy room. That one small stumble changed the direction of the consultation and in turn was to change the direction of things in the coming months.

Dr Gilhooly asked about my loss of balance and how I was managing day to day. I opened up immediately, almost with relief. I explained about fatigue and what it was like for me doing the four nursery runs each day. I spoke with some emotion about life with MS having a bit of a kick at me. I talked about the fairly dramatic changes since Elliot had gone to nursery. I hadn't planned on saying any of that, but that one little stumble seemed to allow me to drop the impression I sometimes gave that I was continually doing well. I was open and honest with Dr Gilhooly, who observed I was struggling a little more than before. The addition of the daily travelling had made my fatigue a greater issue of concern again and put a lot of pressure on my walking. On top of that was the loss of the pram, which was having an enormous impact. The arrival of winter compounded everything.

Dr Gilhooly had been informing me for some time about a procedure to treat something called CCSVI (chronic cerebrospinal venous insufficiency). It was a relatively new procedure, only available in other parts of Europe and further afield up until that time. I had been researching and it was most definitely something that interested me. CCSVI is based on the principle that some people have 'obstructed blood flow in the veins that drain the central nervous system'.[11] They may have veins that are narrow contributing to that. The procedure treats any such obstructions. It was going to cost a lot, but I would judge that to be a good use of money. It was a chance for life to possibly get better. Just the thought of that was enough for me to surge on. The results were mainly favourable and there were numerous testimonials stating the positive benefits. The procedure offered hope to me – and that was indeed priceless.

Dr Gilhooly and his medical team had brought the procedure to the UK, to an Edinburgh-based location. I must state clearly that I believe a great deal of research

11 www.ccsvi.org: CCSVI Alliance, The Basics, What is CCSVI?

and development had gone into bringing the procedure here, as well as capital. I had gathered extensive evidence from numerous sources to help me make an informed and considered decision. Even though the procedure had started to be carried out here in Scotland, Dr Gilhooly and his team had an uphill struggle to have it accepted. Unsurprisingly, it was met with the usual scepticism amongst many in the medical world. The big argument was whether MS patients in fact have CCSVI and if it is linked in any way as a contributing cause of MS. The condition was discovered by an Italian doctor, Dr Zamboni, who claimed that many people with Multiple Sclerosis also have narrowed veins in their neck that could cause difficulty with the flow of oxygen.[12] Now it would be fair to say that most medical information goes right over my head. I think though where the point has been missed by so many is that it does not matter to the person with MS what complicated medical terminology this procedure is explained in, or whether it is the cause or not. It further does not matter if people without MS too have narrowed veins. The fundamental position remains that if there is a lack of blood flow and therefore oxygen through my veins, I will suffer fatigue as well as other symptoms. Anything to alleviate that would help me manage my MS. That was therefore an attractive proposition regardless of the criticism and cynicism around. It is much easier to rubbish something when you are not the person desperately seeking its success for your own personal potential and needs. I truly believe professionals in the

---

12 www.ctvnews.ca: The Liberation Treatment: A whole new
   approach to MS, Avis Favaro, Elizabeth St. Philip, 21.11.2009

medical world would approach so much differently if they were the ones facing a debilitating future.

Many medical professionals have argued that there have been no clinical trials to show the outcomes of this procedure for patients. No major organisation, at the time, was prepared to fund large clinical trials. The neurological world refused to even consider this theory in relation to Multiple Sclerosis. That left those of us with this disease to consider whether we should go ahead and have the procedure done privately or if in fact it was something that could be afforded.

Dr Gilhooly and his team were endeavouring to gather clinical evidence, whilst carrying out the procedures themselves, by collecting data and outcomes. There were plenty of testimonials and anecdotal evidence around. It would cost me several thousand pounds and so I had to make a careful and informed choice. It was a risk of course, but so in fact are many things in life. A lot of medical operations and treatments offer only improvement and not a cure, especially in the face of debilitating and progressive disease. Little in life would move forward, particularly in the medical world, if no one was willing to take part in any new procedure. The first thing to do was have the neck scan to see if I had CCSVI and would be suitable for the procedure. Dr Gilhooly could organise a scan date at relatively short notice. I had only one week to wait. I left the consultation with my head in a spin, but reassured myself that I would put any further decision-making aside until after the results.

The day arrived and I was slightly nervous and slightly excited at the same time. It was a non-invasive ultrasound scan of the whole neck area. I was in my early forties and with a young son of only four; it was imperative I was as well and able as I possibly could be. As Elliot grew, so did the demands of motherhood. My daily routine was suddenly moved outside the comfort and safety of my home. I did not want to just manage my own life and my family life. It is simply honest to say that at times it had only just been manageable up until then. Instead, I wanted to be able to live my life with energy and enthusiasm. I wanted to be someone who could be an active mum with Elliot. I was full of hope as I had the scan. That was closely followed by the results and my pending decision. Yes, I had CCSVI. My veins were very narrow indeed and so I was reliably informed I could benefit from having the procedure. It seemed a 'no brainer' to me that if you widened my veins to improve the blood flow, then more oxygen would circulate through my body and I would feel better.

A fair bit of time was spent over the coming days discussing whether to go ahead and have the procedure at the Edinburgh Clinic. If I'm honest I knew all along I was going to have it. I am not the sort of person who would let an opportunity that may assist me in this almighty fight pass me by. I had read many testimonials where people with MS had seen a marked improvement. The money would be sourced. I viewed it just as others would invest in a new car or a commodity to improve and enhance their lifestyle. I would invest in this procedure with a view to improving and enhancing mine. Sometimes in life you have to take a chance. You know yourself when that time comes. That was mine. It was a calculated risk.

What I was not expecting was a phone call only a few days before Christmas that year in December 2010 to say there was a space available and the procedure could be carried out on 5th January 2011. My initial thoughts were to hold on a minute, as that was way too fast. We were just about to celebrate Christmas and the arrival of Santa for Elliot and now I was faced with preparing for and financing a medical procedure at short notice. So many things seemed to all happen around the festive period for our family. I hesitantly explained to Allan about the phone call from Dr Gilhooly's clinic and made sure I added in all my thoughts about it. I expressed it was short notice, as well as the time of year it was falling in. I pointed out his work commitments, the need for childcare and the financing of it all at such short notice. I added in anything I could come up with to buy myself a little more time. Allan listened patiently to me, but without further investigation or hesitation he simply said, 'Do it, take the appointment.' By early evening that same day most arrangements were in place. My sister was very much behind the idea of going ahead with it and arranged her work around looking after Elliot, along with Gran. Everyone in my small immediate family rallied together. Everyone chipped in and dropped other plans to step in. We had to pull together financial resources and my brother Ricky stretched himself to make a sizeable contribution. We really did work well as a team. I contacted the clinic to tell them I would go ahead at short notice and at that time of year. I went to bed a little apprehensive that night. After all it was me who was going to have the procedure in little less than two weeks!

As always, we had a lovely Christmas and Elliot was as happy as can be. We had fine wines and foods and lots of family gatherings. We were a small team, but a tight one and there always seemed a lot of strength to pull on when it was needed.

We drove through to Edinburgh on the morning of the 4th of January 2011. We arrived in plenty of time for my pre-procedure consultation. The clinic was a large renovated townhouse in a rather leafy and affluent area of Edinburgh. The clinic itself was impressive and if anything, I felt overwhelmed by the whole occasion and the surroundings. On meeting the vascular surgeon, Dr Reid, he was a rather measured and thoughtful man. He was calm, in control and very clear that the procedure was in its early stages here in Scotland. I was only the fifty-sixth person to have it done in Scotland. He explained it involved a practice known as 'ballooning' in the vascular medical world. A small balloon would be used to inflate my jugular veins. It was keyhole surgery and I would remain awake throughout the procedure. That left me uneasy. The aim was to help improve my blood flow. I can still remember him explaining that it was not known what effects the procedure would have on me as an individual, or my condition. He suggested I try not to have many expectations. He went on to say I should keep my hopes low and stay realistic and grounded. There had been good results reported of the procedure, but we would not know how I would respond to it. He offered no false hope at all, but after meeting Dr Reid I felt great confidence in him. I reiterate that I was not presented with any phoney promises. Just care, medical expertise and hope.

We left the next morning before 7 am to accommodate our drive from Glasgow to Edinburgh. It was very cold with lots of ice and snow around. Allan drove and we didn't talk much. I thought a lot about my dad during the journey and pulled on that to gather my strength. We listened to James Blunt and I did my best not to focus on what lay ahead. I was feeling a little apprehensive, but my way of dealing with such feelings was to block them and just keep going forward without a side glance or thought. Just do it. And I did.

The nurse called me after a rather long, agitated wait, in which Allan and I talked and laughed about the most inappropriate and strangest of things. We always did in strained times. Without giving it any thought whatsoever I glanced back at Allan and said in a nonchalant manner, 'See you on the other side!'

I was on my own after that to get prepared for the procedure, before being given the anaesthetic. Those few minutes seemed to go on for a very long time. There were a few tears starting so I had to close down on myself and push on to get that ever-anticipated anaesthetic, which would put me at ease. It did. Within seconds of being given it, my body just melted down into the theatre table and I was in the hands of Dr Gilhooly's clinical team.

They were good hands to be in. The anaesthetist was with me every step of the procedure. That ensured I was comfortable the whole time as I remained conscious throughout. He was an extremely professional yet caring doctor who made a huge difference to how I coped and lessened my fears. I was thankfully drowsy and rather lucid throughout. That helped me cope as the small balloon happened to burst inside my neck! In my listless state, I felt a sudden pop and pulling sensation in my neck. I don't think you can be startled whilst in that physical condition, but a dampened level of confusion came over me. What did that mean? Being me, I tried to ask even in my subconscious state. I always need to know everything and be in control! Another balloon was inflated and the medical world carried on as normal. Panic over – or for them no panic at all! The procedure lasted less than an hour. It didn't feel a long time because of the drugs. I heard voices and words, but couldn't make much sense of them. I had been rather anxious leading up to it, but it was merely uncomfortable at points and not painful as anticipated. My fear was primarily because I was conscious throughout the procedure. But the anaesthetist made sure I was well looked after and my body settled.

I spent some time in the recovery room and very little of that was sleeping. I was having waves in and out of consciousness as I had been throughout the whole procedure, until the anaesthetic began to wear off. I was very unsteady on my feet when I tried to get up after a couple of hours. I wanted to go back to Allan so I did my best to manage. Let's just say my reaction and movement initially did not fill me with optimism. I was stiff, sore and almost mechanical in motion. I gently returned to the patient and family room. I was uncomfortable at that point with other patients and their families being around in the same room. I wanted privacy with Allan. The clinic could not accommodate seclusion and so that was just the way it was set up to be. It was much like a very large living room filled with sofas and tables. It was noticeable for its lamps and mirrors and had a distinctively non-medical feel to it. Maybe I was focussed on the opulence and physical appearance because I was not familiar with the private medical world.

Around the room, other families talked and listened intently to each other's stories. I met some very nice people over the two days. They were all strikingly down to earth. Nearly everyone I spoke with was like-minded in their approach to managing MS. We all shared the same hope and we were all willing to give it a shot. Allan was able to take over things when I returned. I had my security blanket back with me! Surprisingly I found myself to be very hungry! It all felt surreal at that point as I sat on the large, comfortable sofa with my sandwiches and the odd glance over from fellow people with MS and their folks. Allan got me a cup of green tea and I settled myself for what would be a lengthy wait. I didn't feel very good to be honest. It was already a long day and there was still a good bit to go. Allan and my family at home were all desperate to know how I felt. I was pretty much exhausted and weak. It was time to rest.

We were staying at a hotel in Edinburgh that night, as part of the arrangements in order to return the following day for a post-procedure consultation with Dr Reid. I couldn't wait to get to the hotel room. Eventually after a very long day we were told I had recovered enough to leave the clinic. I was frail and unstable all the way travelling to the hotel, but just delighted to arrive at our room and settle for the evening. It was not a comfortable journey, but a manageable one. If you want to reap the benefit of any medical procedure, there will always be a physical and emotional cost. I was doing all right considering. I was getting a little stronger as the anaesthetic wore off. My mood was lifting as I felt relief it was over and the security of being in our hotel room with nothing to do but rest. It was a lovely cosy room and once I had rested for a while, dare I say it, I was starting to feel quite good. We had room service and I even treated myself to a cheeky glass of red! It was strangely a very relaxed and enjoyable evening in our hotel room. I surrendered to the fact I couldn't do anything. Within a short while I entered what was to be a long-awaited deep marshmallow sleep. I still recall that feeling of complete submission as I curled up and gave in to my body shutting down after the procedure, drugs, stress and of course the glass of wine! I shouldn't have had the wine, but that is who I am. Rules and regulations are made to be bent if not broken! From time to time at least!

I felt a tinge of pressure in the morning. Obviously, I wanted so much to feel there was some positive change and be able to share some good news with my family. I had energy immediately on waking up and the best way to describe it was that my joints felt like they had been oiled! My brain did not carry with it that MS 'cloud' it would normally have. My movement was improved and I felt good. My spirits were high and I was optimistic. I was in a fine mood and made contact to let those waiting on news know how I was feeling. It was very early days, but the initial signs were encouraging.

We made our way back to the Edinburgh Clinic and met with Dr Reid. He was again very cautious in his approach, but said that the procedure had gone well and he had ballooned my veins successfully. He had also treated an area where there was reflux in my blood flow. Overall my blood flow should now be improved. He commented that he noticed a positive change in my physical appearance. I myself did not feel that normal drained and tired way I had become so familiar with. I left with cautious optimism.

From there we made our way home to Glasgow. We did have one stop at an inviting supermarket. I couldn't resist and collected champagne, treats and something for everyone, especially Elliot! I rarely needed an excuse. It would be fair to say I felt on a real high and I was never one to suggest keeping your feet on the ground for too long! A happy and positive day lay ahead and I wanted everyone to indulge in it. We surely deserved to. Although the next few days were exciting, they also came with some apprehension. It was all very emotional and I was coping with a lot of stuff. I was very aware not to let myself go sky-high with my emotions and energy and do too much. The very focussed doctor had explained to me that the aim was to retain some consistency as well as rest for the initial period. I had listened carefully and followed his instructions to the letter.

My increased levels of energy stayed with me and the heavy cloud that lived in my head was lifted and lighter. That is often referred to as 'brain fog' in people with MS and it appeared very different. It felt like I was in a new body with the transformation in my joint movement. There is a lot of stiffness and rigidity attached to MS and so that was a very real change. That brought some tears with the many emotions flying around me. I knew there was little evidence around of how things would continue to be over the coming months. It was all a pioneering experience. I was determined not to get carried away and burn out. I rested as directed for the first few days, but enjoyed my new sense of feeling lighter and less burdened than before. After the first week, I set to starting a new exercise and swimming routine. My aim was to ensure that I exercised with consistency. That too had been advised to keep up the new improved blood flow. With little unforeseen exceptions for periods of time, I have tried to keep up that exercise routine with renewed effort ever since.

It is difficult to say with exact precision what benefits and effects the CCSVI procedure had on me in the longer term. The initial feelings of improved mobility and flexibility did last some time. I experienced a big surge in energy for many months after the procedure, which allowed me to enjoy a much higher quality of life. I travelled more and was far more ambitious with what I did. Time passed and I did not maintain those early benefits in their entirety. However, I did not return to my pre-CCSVI state of health either. There is not a definitive science in any of that, but a feeling of overall well-being and improved quality of life. Every time I'm having a not-so-good mobility day or my balance is particularly poor, I always remind myself of my crippling fatigue and brain fog before my CCSVI procedure. The procedure was a big part of my MS journey. Elliot was almost five and starting school that year. It was perfect timing to give me a boost in both energy and mobility to prepare me for school life. Not to mention having some well-earned and yearned-for fun.

I have kept in touch with one person I met at the clinic who still carries the belief that the CCSVI procedure was a positive factor in their MS journey too. There was one other woman who was restricted by her mobility to a wheelchair. I met her at Dr Gilhooly's clinic some six months on at the follow-up appointment. She was full of smiles and enthusiasm and went on to explain that the debilitating fatigue she had endured for many years had almost all but been lifted. There had been no change to her mobility, but the most enormous transition had been made through her diminished fatigue. She was satisfied overall with the CCSVI procedure and the very real improvement in her quality of life.

The treatment was erroneously dubbed the 'liberation procedure' which did not help matters at all. I was not looking for a cure. I was looking for some improvement. I got it and I am so glad I made the decision to go ahead and have it. It is suggested that CCSVI goes some way to 'exploiting desperate patients'.[13] There is no known cure for MS and very little constructive treatment available. Surely, we should be encouraging research and funding clinical trials into any procedures or medicines that might help people like myself and improve our quality of life. People are too quick to condemn and close the door on what cannot be conclusively proven, scientifically and medically. Aside from the fact that hope is everything when it comes to living with a chronic disease, many would say that any improvement I experienced was nothing more than the placebo effect. If that were the

13 www.sciencebasedmedicine.org: Update on CCSVI and Multiple Sclerosis, Steven Novella, 26.10.2016

simplistic answer, I'm sure my placebo effect would have generated a greater improvement in my symptoms! Perhaps even a cure! Patients like myself need to be given more respect and trust in our decision-making. I was not handing over thousands of pounds in desperation and without grave consideration. I was making a very informed choice. I had amassed professional and personal advice. I was having an extremely well-sourced procedure in the UK by GMC-qualified and vetted medics who had many years' expertise and practice.

The procedure is no longer available in the UK. The regulatory body NICE (National Institute for Clinical Excellence) decided that it could only take place in the UK under the condition of clinical trials, even though there were many positive outcomes reported from patients. The medical authorities are not prepared to fund trials. So, there will be no further procedures taking place here in the UK for the time being. Therefore, no one else with MS can have the choice and opportunity anymore that was given to me. I'm not sure that decision is fair or right. I was in the hands of a formidable medical team. Those were doctors of the highest calibre.

So, was it the right decision to have the CCSVI procedure? It certainly was. Was it worth the money? Every last penny. Would I do it again? Tomorrow.

16

Post-CCSVI

'Go out on a limb. That's where the fruit is.'

(Jimmy Carter)

I had some exciting energy about me over the months that followed my CCSVI procedure and it was purely a matter of *what* I should do, rather than *if* I should do something. With my renewed spirit and stamina, I went overboard and booked many weekends away and trips out because I was feeling so well and able. It was with great enthusiasm I dived into the new opportunities available to me. There was immense relief that as a family we could get to experience parts of life that had categorically been off the menu since MS barged into our lives.

I wanted to travel some more, perhaps just Elliot and me? That was a bit radical, but I felt up for it for the first time in years. I planned to go and visit my friend Liz who lived just outside London. We shared a flat together while we were teaching and living in Spain. We both had boys now and what could be more fun than a few days with three boys aged four, five and six years old? I'm not sure if it would be in fact relaxing, but fun nonetheless! Allan and others were just a little unsure if it was a good idea or not. I was confident. Booked and planned, the time soon arrived. Elliot had just turned five; he was full of energy, ideas and was great company!

I will always remember that trip as it was a landmark in my MS journey. It was the first thing of any real significance I had done independently since my diagnosis. I'm afraid it's just not feasible to suggest that after five years living with my symptoms, I could travel independently with Elliot purely because of an imagined placebo effect. The whole trip was in fact exhilarating for me. Elliot was delighted to be going to the airport and on holiday to see his friends Jonathan and Zachary. We travelled excitedly by plane to Gatwick. I was feeling very well and in control. That trip is what I will always be able to measure the success of my CCSVI procedure by. I could never have contemplated such a trip, on my own with all the needs of a five-year-old, prior to my procedure. Never.

I probably didn't explain fully the impact of my MS to my friend. I was feeling well and both Liz and her husband commented on how well I looked and was doing. Living with MS was like surfing the waves all the time. At that moment, I found myself on the crest of a wave and decided to stay there. We travelled on the train, the Underground, went for a play in Green Park and visited the Natural History Museum, all on a day trip to London! I had to stop and start a fair bit, but it went largely unnoticed. I had to be careful too with my footing in the park, but again I managed to carry it off. Elliot was only five so we walked hand in hand much of the day. I rested on and off and we stopped for refreshments on more than one occasion. When my legs got heavy and troublesome to lift, it was mind over matter and time to round off the day. On the train home I felt exhausted, but it had been a full day and only the three boys were, I think, more tired than me! It doesn't end there. Liz had to take the dog out on our return home so I stayed with the boys, gave them a bath and got them ready for bed. I sure was punching above my weight! In fact, I think I would go as far as to say it was as close as I ever got to feeling like a 'regular' mum. With the boys so tired they fell asleep just after seven, we sat down with a glass of wine for a chat and catch-up. It really did feel normal at that point. I didn't last much past nine o'clock, but all in all I felt that a bit of me from before MS had returned. Even if it was only for a visit.

It felt good not to be relying on others and I loved travelling by myself with Elliot. I certainly was at my peak after the procedure. I had a good few months on my return from our trip. The nursery runs were managed with a little more ease. My fatigue showed the biggest improvement. That in turn fed into all the other aspects of life. We went as an extended family to a villa in Andalucía. The holiday had its moments, but again I managed exceptionally well. I indulged in many outings and trips around Scotland over the summer months. I did get a new lease of life. I was not able to sustain all of that in the longer term. However, I chose to revel in the fact that it happened rather than be disappointed that it did not continue at the same level of energy and ability.

The CCSVI procedure had made a significant impact and we had to look at ways to prolong and sustain its benefits. With the school years for Elliot just around the corner we needed to prepare as much as possible. There was no point trying to convince ourselves it would be all right and fall into place when school started. We had to be much more practical and prepare for what was our reality. With that in mind we decided to take a close look at Allan's employment status. Allan had always immersed himself in his work and been very committed. He was successful in his field of training and consultancy. It would be reasonable to say he was tiring of the everyday politics attached to his working life at times. I had been wrestling daily with the bus journeys to and from nursery. I was trying to move away from the bit where I battled through daily tasks to one where I had a better day-to-day life. I did not want my future to be one big struggle. So, we made the critical decision that Allan would leave his job at the university and set up on his own. That came after a great deal of consideration. It was of course a risk. In many ways, we had no choice but to take it. It would ease the pressures on the domestic front with school life pending and all that would bring with it.

Allan made the move and set up his own company. It has been a long and slow road. He has worked extremely hard with extended working hours and built it up almost single-handed. He has done an exceptional job to establish and maintain a small business in the difficult financial climate of the time. He managed to achieve that whilst supporting his wife with MS, not to mention a young child growing up and all that required, too. Allan is the only person I can think of who would have the resilience, commitment and ability to manage such adversity.

The whole thing brought with it financial challenges as well as working unsociable hours. We had gone from two above-average salaries to a small pension and payment day by day on contract work for Allan. He had to build the business from nothing. There were many financial ups and downs on our already fraught journey. Those were the hidden outcomes of having a chronic condition. There was no choice available to us that would not impact in some way or other. We had to make the best of our situation. Having less money paled into insignificance compared to having health and ability. On a positive note, the job change served to alleviate other stresses. The most noticeable of those being that Allan would be around more for the school runs with the car. He could now do his working hours when it was more suitable to our family needs. Allan would sometimes have to work on a Saturday afternoon or late into the evening. That was the price we had to pay so he could be about mid-week to offer support as and when required. We missed out on some family times at weekends, but it was a small sacrifice compared to some of those days, for me, battling the weather and journeys to and from nursery.

That has been our most far-reaching decision yet in relation to the changes we have had to make. It came about because we had Elliot and that brings with it all the things you must arrange and do when raising a child. Most of those daily activities people take for granted, but that was no longer a privilege of mine or indeed Allan's. He worked hard continuously and it would be true to say we had less free time overall, as that came with the territory of running your own small business.

If you look at it from a different angle, we were very pro-active in our plans and in executing them to allow us not just to manage our situation, but to have a fulfilled and rewarding family life. Both the CCSVI procedure and the decision for Allan to become self-employed gave us those opportunities.

17

Elliot Starts School

'Why fit in when you were born to stand out?'

(Dr. Seuss)

The time arrived to enrol Elliot at school. The next step along the road was laid down for him. We had prepared as best we could to cope with all the changes that were to come. The 16th August 2011 arrived for Elliot's first day at St Rose of Lima Primary School in Glasgow. The school gates were at the bottom of the steep hill and a further distance to travel than the nursery. Hills did not see me at my best, but Allan would be about a lot more to take Elliot to school in the car. I would take him and collect him only on the days Allan had to work away. School came with a list of challenges, but it was still an exciting time. Although I would miss Elliot dearly, I would embrace the new experiences ahead alongside the hurdles. I have always loved delving into different phases of motherhood and each new chapter of Elliot's development.

I did think I should maybe tell the school and some of the parents I knew about my MS. I only glanced over that idea, as I did not want to be known as Elliot's mum, the one with MS. I did not want to be treated differently and most certainly not looked on with pity, concern or judged on my wavering ability. I would just be Elliot's mum, plain and simple. You would take me as you find me and I had no need to explain myself. My mum and dad had always taught me to 'celebrate difference' and that was all I would expect of others. I made my decision not to tell anyone and I would manage any outcomes of that decision. I had a lot of experience of education and schools from many years of teaching and felt I had a lot to offer a school. Not sure any staff at the school ever shared the same view! Nevertheless, it was very important to me to be seen not as a mum with a chronic disease, but as plainly another mum and contributor. People make assumptions and judgements, which is clearly wrong, but still accepted in many circles. The safest way to avoid any issues and be treated as an equal was not to tell anyone.

School life started in earnest after a few weeks when Elliot went in for full days. He was not a great fan of school from the beginning. There were to be many difficulties for both Elliot and me over the coming years. On the days I dropped him off and picked him up, it brought about the same hurdles as nursery. As always, that included walking up and down the steep hill. I managed the journeys for the most part, but there were some unexpected days that brought with them unrivalled challenges.

On what was a regular Monday morning, early in the first school term, we set off for the bus stop. As always we had a spring in our step and got onto the bus for our usual morning quiz! My legs didn't feel at their strongest, but hey ho, that was not unusual. As we walked down the hill towards the school we met different folks and stopped to say hello, for which I was glad of the short rest. I had Elliot's hand to steady me walking downwards. We got into the school at the bottom of the steep hill and I was visibly unsteady and drained. Walking across the open yard was not an easy task, but thankfully Elliot was off playing and unaware. I tried to carry on as close to normal as I could get, but I just wanted the playground to be empty so I could gather and compose myself. That wasn't going to happen, but as the bell rang and Elliot reluctantly went into class I felt some sense of relief. I walked and talked to another mum. I don't possess the skill to do both simultaneously and so I felt more relaxed when she had to go in a different direction at the gate. I was sadly trying to fit in and keep up appearances at the time. I still had the hill to climb in front of me. There just seemed no power in my legs. My balance was way out of step, but I kept going and I really did sway most of the way. My legs would just not do what I asked of them and I staggered backwards with every step I took. That is life with a disease like MS. There can be no rhyme or reason to what's happening that day and no choice but to keep going, however it may look to the outside world passing by.

The positive outcome of me being so slow and uncoordinated was that all the other parents from school were long gone as I clambered my way up the rather bleak hill. So at least there was no one about to witness my struggle. The surrounding area was open and flat once you reached the top. It was a rather grey and dull day as I crossed the very sparse area towards the bus stop. I stayed on my feet until I banged back against the bus stop shelter with some relief. An elderly lady, herself with a little difficulty walking, said 'It's like the living dead around here!' and we laughed. She had obviously noticed my struggle. My laugh was a nervous, awkward one. There I was seen in the same bracket as the elderly! I didn't mind. It was just nice to be accepted and not judged. All I wanted was to get home where I could gather myself together. After all, I needed to recover somewhat to be ready to do it all again at three o'clock!

On more days than not Allan takes Elliot to school by car. That sort of extreme day does not happen all the time, but when it does it just lands on me. It made me realise the school days ahead were going to ask a lot of me. As much as I had prepared for what was to come, Multiple Sclerosis can have a mind of its own. I stayed positive and focussed with school life and being involved, but I was on higher alert following that day. I learned to respond on a day-to-day basis as necessary. I took it in my stride, didn't over-analyse and carried on my determined path.

School life for me as Elliot's mum was never going to be straightforward in more ways than just the physical barriers. I hold very definite views on child development and education and these do not always fall in line with that of mainstream education. Addressing school issues, attending school events and taking part in school life all brought about additional bus journeys as well as more walking and mobility challenges. They also meant I had more episodes of dizziness and fatigue. I had to dig deep to negotiate walking, talking and thinking all at the same time. It was challenging to say the least. My legs let me down more than once, failing to work at the end of meetings, discussions and school events. I just had to stumble and rather robotically move as best I could. My legs tend to stiffen up when I am sitting for a prolonged period or where there is any stress involved. It can even be down to the height of the chair I am sitting on.

Those experiences make life much harder and push my limits, but they are all part of my life with Multiple Sclerosis. I want to be a fully active parent in school life and wouldn't miss out on a thing that involves Elliot. My choice to attend, take part and address issues means challenging consequences for me and school life always demands a great deal of strength and courage. It puts my difficulties right out there for everyone to see in situations I don't get to control. The head teacher, Miss Shiels, has been very supportive and forward-thinking over the years. All issues have been addressed with care and passion. Elliot has settled more as time has gone on and I just have to manage the adversity of school life as best I can. There have been plenty of hurdles and though I never quite managed to jump over them, I have always found a way to get around them! Elliot has had lots of positive experiences of school life too, often helped by the exceptional Mrs Foster.

I joined the Parent Council and attended monthly meetings. Again, something where I could have chosen not to take part, especially as meetings were held in the evenings, but that would not have been me. After the first couple of years I took on the role of Chair. I helped organise meetings and fundraising events along with other parents and played a full part. That pushed the boundaries of my physical ability, but I have always met every challenge head on. I have not had many negative experiences as part of the Parent Council. Groups like that are not my thing, but I wanted to be able to monitor Elliot's school life so I had to put myself forward. There was one occasion when another mum took my arm to guide me along the corridor to the school hall without consulting me. I was so surprised and concentrating on being able to manage the physical layout in front of me that I did not challenge her. I recognised there was no intent to cause offence. She undoubtedly thought she was helping me, but was in fact patronising me. People need to learn it is acceptable to do things differently. If someone is uncomfortable with that, the issue lies with them. We must not merely tolerate difference, but celebrate it in all walks of life. I am a grown woman who is confident and independent. If I need help, I will ask.

I volunteered to take part in a school project over ten weeks, involving training days and evenings working with and supporting families within the school. I did question myself, again only briefly, if I had on that occasion taken a step too far. There was a lot of walking and physical expectation of my involvement. I managed, but was exhausted at the end of each evening accompanied by lead legs after my over-exertion. Despite all of that, I thoroughly enjoyed volunteering, being active and involved in something positive. I love learning and relish all opportunities to do so. On the final evening I was expected to walk onto a small school stage to receive a gift in gratitude for my voluntary work. I was in fact faced with the situation where I could not walk up the two small steps, as there was no support at either side. I very calmly asked the community worker, Tina, from my group to go up again on my behalf to collect my gift. She never asked why nor gave it any attention, but went ahead and did it for me. The way she did made all the difference to me that evening and I was not left feeling different or excluded. So, there is nothing I have not taken part in or volunteered for in school life. I could have seen my MS as a barrier, but that is just not in my DNA. My decision not to tell teachers and parents allowed me to be able to take part freely and no one else could put up barriers for me. An absolute crucial point in this entire journey.

As the years passed I found myself thinking of ways to make school life more manageable. I approached Elliot's teacher, Mrs Kiernan, at the primary 3 stage. I wanted to ask if she could assist by allowing me to meet Elliot at the school office a few minutes before home time on the days I collected him. That would cut my hill-walking journey in half. It was a very small matter, but hugely significant in my circumstances. I found myself to be surprisingly nervous when speaking to her as I felt I had to offer a reason why I wanted to make that arrangement. She had no idea I had never asked anyone for help outside of close family. It was a big deal to me and in the end I said, 'I have mobility issues.' Her reaction to my request was solely one word: 'Anything'. The arrangement was put in place and there were no questions asked. To date she has never asked a question nor passed any comment. That is the kind of support people need, where they are not made to feel different, special or indeed that they are being granted some big favour for simply having an alternative need.

I will always be grateful to Mrs Kiernan for her non-judgemental, non-patronising and supportive manner.

As Elliot grew up he became more resilient and coped better with school life. We worked hard to reduce the need for trips up and down to school, which surely helped me cope. It would be dishonest not to admit though that Elliot's primary school years stretched me to my limits with MS. I continued to be involved in school life and felt able to take part in more and worried less about how I would manage as time went on. I just did. I am 'differently abled', not disabled. I am able to do almost everything, but put simply I do things differently. The world would be a better place if everyone started to think that way.

18

Disbelief

'But then I have always been somewhat of a square peg in a round hole.'

(*Cressida Cowell*)

Throughout this journey, from the very first symptom I experienced, my gallant spirit and gritty determination have been with me. I have though, disappointingly, still succumbed to trying to fit in as 'normal' on some occasions. I have done so because there are many people around who are more inclined to treat you differently when they know you have a medical condition. Over time, and much to my disbelief, I found that out the hard way. I tried to hide my condition in the earlier days. I wanted to keep life as straightforward as possible for Elliot. I refused to be treated differently, so it was better not to be open. That way people did not have the opportunity to offend or exclude. I have tried to fit in, particularly throughout Elliot's school life. I made great efforts to keep up with others and put a lot of unnecessary pressure on myself. That made things more problematic and took its toll on me. Despite my debilitating fatigue I still pushed my body beyond acceptable physical limits trying to keep up appearances. I would grit my teeth to keep moving forward. If I were being honest, I would admit that I would do the same things all over again. It is who I am and I believe there are no limits we shouldn't go to for what we want. I also believe that accepting and changing are part of a process. I have had to go some way in that process to realise I could not keep up the pace of the earlier days.

I do find great difficulty when anyone treats me differently. I don't think as a society we cater for people's differing needs. We should. Ever since I have had MS it has struck me how hard it is to fit in with everyday life. It has been difficult to accept the amount of times I have been harassed on an escalator stair. Or on a flight of stairs. Or on a narrow walkway. The list is endless. I obviously don't move fast enough for the rest of the world. They were never slow to let me know. It could be rather disconcerting, but as time has gone on I just let them huff and puff and don't react anymore. I used to try to get out of the way and usually without much grace. Now I just stay where I am and smile. People are too quick to judge and expect everyone to be able to manage the same way that they can. I'm afraid that's just not possible for us all.

I have arrived for school events and felt excluded as there was limited or no seating. I have found myself unable to make my way to the designated area independently without railings or support. There is just an assumption made throughout life that everyone can fit the main criteria. That is clearly not the case, but in our society if you can't fit in, for the most part, you are excluded.

I refuse to accept that status and usually battle my way through, but it is not a nice or kind place to be.

Every time I slumped down in a taxi, the driver had a shifty look to check if I was in fact under the influence of alcohol. Once I sat up and chatted they were left wondering what that was all about! I have been stopped in the street and told I was a disgrace out with my young son 'like that'. Obviously implying I was under the influence of alcohol or drugs. Disappointed I may have been and a little disheartened that I live in a world that is not as nice as I would like it to be. However, I am very able to separate my thoughts and feelings and realise those people are ignorant. Most people are not like that.

I have been asked time and time again 'Are you all right?' simply because I am off balance or because I walk differently or because I am somewhat withdrawn. It is undoubtedly taxing and challenging to live that way and be questioned continuously. It rarely feels out of concern, but borders more on curiosity or even worse pity. There is no point to the question purely because someone is different. The answer is clearly and loudly 'Yes, I am all right in *my little MS world.*' It can be difficult, but it is nonetheless the world I live in. We need to accept people with their different abilities and ways of doing things. I was asked once along with that question 'but what if you fall?' I don't think they were too impressed when I answered 'Then I'll get back up!' We can't just sit in the corner in case something happens and because we have a chronic disease! Life is a risk! Life is different for everyone. Don't assume that one life is better or more valuable than another purely based on the fact it is different. I would not swap my life with Allan and Elliot for anything. With or without Multiple Sclerosis.

I have lost count of the times I have gone into a city centre small supermarket chain store, only to be followed by the security officer on duty because of my unruly balance. That has happened time and time again. It does not happen in the bigger supermarkets as I can hide behind the grocery trolley. In a city centre store I must rely on the shopping basket. I have grown a little impatient of this. Just because my balance is poor I should not be judged. Personally, I do not think people should be judged full stop. On one occasion, I was followed and gawked at by a female security guard. When I got to the checkout I noticed her signal to the assistant not to serve me alcohol. Maybe it's just me, but I think it is plainly obvious I am not under the influence of alcohol. The truly awful experience is the fact that others are making negative judgements and assumptions about me based on a physical appearance I have no control over. It gave me a glimpse of what many suffer across a broad spectrum. I did have wine in my basket that day as my mum was coming over for dinner. I had no intention of having a glass. It is inconceivable that I should have to explain such circumstances. But I did and the security guard shuffled quickly into the back store once I announced in front of staff and shoppers that I had Multiple Sclerosis! Hopefully she heard my call to 'Just ask next time' before she left the shop floor! On first glance someone may be excused for thinking I was under the influence, but after that it doesn't take a lot to work out that my mobility issues are not related to drugs or alcohol. Surely by today's standards we would think and try to ascertain facts before jumping to conclusions? That does not seem to be a common occurrence. I think it goes back to people's ignorance and stereotyping. I will say though that it is exhausting from my point of view as well as aggravating. We need to educate people better and raise the bar on the general public's awareness. People are too quick to judge and frown on what does not fit their pre-conceived ideas. Being different is acceptable and normal too.

In order to truly accept different abilities, people, schools, organisations and society at large need to make provisions to include everyone. Currently, that simply does not happen. Inclusion seems to be an afterthought for most. Exclusion has been the standard model in my experience. Until people and organisations realise that 'different ability' comes in many forms, I believe life will continue to leave a great many people out. People's intention to act seems only to be drawn to the stereotype of a wheelchair user. Even then the provision made leaves a great deal to be desired. There are so many of us who wish to be independent, but are hindered in doing so by society's unwillingness to make alternative arrangements.

When it came to being included and accepted I did not anticipate encountering difficulties with my friends. I was wrong. Many friendships were to diminish or indeed come to an abrupt ending. Most were friendships built on different facets particular to the time and place I found myself living in. Almost all relationships were affected by my diagnosis. Only a few were close friendships and they did not stand the test of time. Most definitely not the difficult times I had to face up to. That goes for friendships of just a few years as well as those that have existed much longer. It is not true of everyone of course. My friend Liz, who I met in Spain, is the only one from all my years travelling that I have stayed in touch with beyond social media. The only other exceptions are my friends, Alison and Helen, from my youth and school days. Both have stayed in touch over the years through letter-writing and visits back and forth. Alison is the most loyal person and there are no lengths she would not go to for me. Helen is non-judgemental in every way and almost doesn't notice my MS.

I did not understand why my friends had such difficulty with my news. If I'm honest, I still feel that way. I expected a huge wall of strength and care to come my way, but instead it was just a big empty space with not a lot going on. I realised in fact I had met many acquaintances and shared some good times, but it had been little more than that. One by one they made less and less contact and I started to get the message. The replies to my texts began to dry up too. I did feel some anger and disappointment, but it was not proportionate to the loss I was encountering.

Nothing had changed about me except their perception. It was a steep learning curve, but one I got the hang of quickly. I am in touch with very few people nowadays. I spend my time and energy with Elliot, Allan and my immediate family. Having a chronic disease renders you with little left for others. I have learned the lesson that if you manage to make one or two real friends in your life you have done well, as the rest are just companions sharing a time with you. Many people are much more ready and willing to share the good times. When adversity strikes, I have found they tend to make themselves scarce. I have no problem with that anymore. I am self-sufficient. I have rekindled some relationships through social media. Elizabeth and Lorna have met me exactly where I was at on every occasion, in relation to life in general and Multiple Sclerosis. Total acceptance and adapting without being asked. Emma too. There are never any questions, judgements or even opinions in relation to my MS. That is what I needed from all my friends, old and new, but it was not to be.

I have tried to just be myself and not focus on fitting in more and more as time has gone on. Friends, acquaintances and strangers alike must accept me for who I am and all that comes with that. I will not give in to being excluded, but at the same time I do choose my battles, as it is entirely exhausting constantly challenging people and situations. I am no longer in disbelief. I see clearly a society that operates on the 'survival of the fittest'. I reject that society, I always did. I am focussed on what *I can* do and achieve. I am still the very same person I was before my diagnosis. I have the same rights and responsibilities I had prior to MS. I have the same thoughts and aspirations. I will meet everything head on, just as I would have prior to Multiple Sclerosis.

19

wecanfindaway.com

*'Obstacles don't have to stop you. If you run into a wall,
don't turn around and give up. Figure out how to climb it,
go through it, or work around it.'*

(Michael Jordan)

With the wecanfindaway.com attitude and outlook I
have been focussed on staying independent and dealing
with life as it happens. In the absence of support from
friends and society in general, I have relied on myself
and eventually accepted support from my immediate
family. I have always been a feisty, independent woman
so I had plenty of practice behind me! In the early days,
I was not as willing or able to accept support from
anyone. I needed to prove to myself and others I was still
that capable and independent person. A great deal of
frustration comes from the way our society is structured
not to facilitate different needs. That leaves people like
myself struggling to remain independent and carry out
daily tasks. Even something as simple as there not being
a handrail to the entrance of a shop or building with
stairs has excluded me from many places and going to
them unaided. That didn't happen in the early years, but

changed as time has gone on. You have no idea how that makes me feel, particularly after spending the first forty years of my life without those concerns and knowing that with some planning and commitment, so much could be improved.

Through my stubborn determination and sometimes dumfounded stupidity to do things by myself I have managed a great deal. Even on occasions where help would have made a positive difference, I would run myself into the ground before I would ask. Whether that was right or wrong, that is who I was and still am. I didn't ask anyone for anything and I just pushed on no matter what the consequences would be. As time went on I did learn to accept some support, but only on rare occasions and when it was offered. When it comes to having to ask for help it has to be something I simply cannot manage and there are only a handful of immediate family I would turn to. I include Elliot in that handful.

It seems simple enough to say that we all need a little help from time to time. My need had become that bit greater. Being a new mum meant any assistance on offer was most welcome. But in relation to my MS, it was not as easy to gladly receive that helping hand. I continued to do all the things I could in my family. I was the planner and organiser as well as the main cook for family celebrations and the festive period. My very immediate family grew into doing any tasks that required excessive mobility on my part or travelling. I would describe myself as aggressively independent and on almost every occasion, I will fight to find an alternative way of doing something that presents a challenge or obstacle to me. I have never suggested someone else should simply do it for me. But I have, as time has gone on, allowed a few family members to carry out the more demanding tasks.

That support falls to literally a few. My sister is very willing and able to step in at any given point and help. She has on many occasions been the one standing next to me, enabling my balance and presence without anyone knowing. Nothing has ever been too much trouble for her. My mum has facilitated all my complementary therapy visits and medical appointments by playing host to Elliot. She loves spending time with him and vice versa. They have a very special bond and share a somewhat inspiring relationship for two people with such extremes of age. I have on many occasions asked my mum 'to be my legs' and travel to the city centre to collect an online purchase for me. She has always been an enthusiastic help. My brother Ricky is always around for any unforeseen circumstances. I like to keep my support circle small as well as my circumstances private. I would need to be stretched to involve anyone else.

With the exception that is, of course, Allan. We share our lives so it has not been so much about asking for help. If anything, I have had to come to terms more with accepting support as the years have passed. Allan would at best describe me as stubborn when it comes to asking for or receiving help. He may well be more likely to say obstinate! He has learned to work with me side by side and it has been a steep learning curve for us both. There is nothing he would not do for me. Day and night, he has always gone the extra mile and that has been ever since I met him. I need not say anymore.

As Elliot has grown up he has become more aware of his mum's mobility and ability issues. He has been caring, protective and given me limitless support both physically and emotionally ever since. I am certainly proud of how he has developed and indeed managed as a young child whose mum has MS. His support and very importantly understanding were and still are crucial to me.

I am thankful I have such a strong and caring family. It has made a big difference. Between us we have always found a way and that is how I like it. I often thrive on the fact I have to find a way. It gives me focus, purpose and a great sense of achievement. There is invariably an alternative route if you just keep searching. I have been privileged enough to always find the physical and mental strength to succeed. When you discover yourself to be in the vulnerable position I did, you have no time to wait and hope society will include you. Or that it will afford you equal access and opportunity. I will always challenge inequality and exclusion, but at the same time I will always look to my own resources and determination to find a way around whatever obstacles I am met with. It is a rare day when I am presented with none. So rare, I cannot recall such a day.

Trips out with Elliot have always been a priority since he was born. I planned that I would give him as many different experiences as I could. As someone who had spent many years teaching young children I firmly believe that much, if not most, of a child's learning takes place outside of school and therefore the responsibility lies with the parents and carers. With that in mind, as well as a desire to share those experiences and enjoy life with

Elliot, I was always thinking of the next place to visit or thing to do. That was going to be more challenging with Multiple Sclerosis, but most definitely something that would still happen in full. It was simply a case of finding a way to overcome whatever challenges we were faced with. That has been done for the most part and Elliot has had a wealth of different experiences and is developing all the better for them. From simple trips to the seaside, rugby, ballet and much more, I have managed them all. No matter the mobility requirements – the steps, the hills, the crowds or the queues – they have all been invigorating, fun and rewarding. We have always found a way! There have been more challenges with public transport for some trips and a lot of planning involved when it was just Elliot and me. The pram was a crucial contributing factor to enable many of the outings in the early years. After the pram was no longer about I had to consider where we would go. Gran joined us on many of our outings and we travelled by bus, train and boat! It is one of the things I am proudest of in my achievements, that we have visited so many places and taken part in so many activities, despite the fact I have MS. It really has been a case of 'Where there's a will, there's a way'.

The joys of domestic duties do not pass you by, even with a chronic disease diagnosis! There are many more household chores as a family of three. The older Elliot gets, the more sports and clubs he joins bringing mud, mess and of course fun! I must choose which jobs I will do and when. I then have to pace myself according to how I am feeling and what else I have to do that day. I do punch above my weight on most days and manage well. I'm thankful I have the inner strength and drive that keeps me going forward. I do get frustrated that I have to down tools and wait until the next day to carry on or finish a job, but there is nothing I can do to change that. I have tried and tested most conceivable options, but they have all produced the same outcome. I become tired, jaded and woozy. If it's a day I'm collecting Elliot from school, then very little can be done on the domestic front (like I've said, there's always a positive!). I have many reactions to doing many jobs. I become disorientated occasionally, dizzy often and always have a bout of fatigue. There are no words to adequately describe my disappointment, but that is simply the way it is for me. I do less domestically than is sometimes required and I never do anything more often than is necessary. Deep cleaning is rare as the consequences are dire, but must be faced from time to time. Allan does a great deal around the house, but he already works exceedingly long hours running his own small business. Life goes on and we find a way as best we can.

An enormous challenge to me living an ordinary life is eating out. It also became an enormous challenge to the wecanfindaway.com approach. I struggled, and still do, to find a way forward as the catering world let me down, time and time again. It is highlighted more when I am on holiday. I do not have the luxury at those times to return home to prepare food myself, unless of course it is a self-catering holiday. I could write a separate book to describe the numerous and regrettable experiences I have had whilst on holiday, both at home and abroad. It has affected each and every trip whether it was a short or long stay and the problems encountered abroad eventually became insurmountable. Almost all holidays led to substantial weight loss and regular flare-ups of my symptoms. More often than not my legs would become heavy and a struggle to manoeuvre. I cannot stress enough how big an obstacle this is and the impact it has on family life. Let's say it is not a subject I would suggest you bring up with Allan! He has had his patience and trust in people stretched far beyond any reasonable limits. You would expect that simple dietary requirements could be met without a great deal of fuss. That has not proved to be the case. I have been served food on many occasions that has been prepared with the wrong ingredients to suit my dietary needs. I have been told I had to choose from the main menu or eat nothing. I have found myself arguing with the kitchen manager over what is in fact a dairy product. It became obvious that no attention or care was being given to my special requirements. That all happened despite giving notice of those requirements and the medical reason for them. It also happened in mostly four-star, reputable hotels and restaurants. To complicate matters further I am a vegetarian. In many parts of the world, none more so than Scotland, I'm afraid that renders you as some sort of alien being!

This obstacle has proved impossible to overturn. Time and time again the kitchen got it wrong. It has been exasperating. The only option has been to choose to eat at home for the most part and to go on self-catering holidays. Despite the years that have passed it is the one stumbling block we continue to encounter. We did return for a long time to the same Italian where we had our small wedding reception, Sarti's, in Glasgow city centre. I knew the quality of food and oils used were good. However, the toilets were located some way from the restaurant and down some very steep stairs and so that eventually became too risky.

It is important to add that returning to the same eateries and hotels has not always meant having the same experience, positive or negative. Elliot started to become anxious as food was being served, in anticipation of it being returned. That was until a very fine chef, Philipp Albath, at the Hilton Resort in Aviemore took it upon himself to make amends for all our negative and dismal experiences. We were spoiled with VIP treatment for our stay. My food was exceptional and Elliot came away with an abundance of positive memories. It was such a special and unexpected treat. The Malmaison in Edinburgh is a firm favourite of ours. It has always met my requirements and with a smile. We spend our wedding anniversary there whenever we can. Maybe one day the rest of the catering world will stretch its talents to include vegetarians with special dietary requirements? I am not holding my breath though!

The latest challenge presented to me was that indeed of writing my book. That was a very different type of challenge as it interfered with my cognitive performance. I could do the actual writing and pursue that for prolonged periods. It did involve a lot of repetition and revision, but that's just part of the process of some cognitive tasks with a neurological condition. When I stopped, I was very tired with heavy eyes and that would be my activity for the day done. Or at least it should have been, but I tended not to pay much heed to the warning signs. When

I finished writing, and started to walk away from the laptop immediately I would be off balance. More often than not the room would go for a little spin around me. I was always exceptionally tired mentally. A headache became a regular occurrence and something I had to get used to living with. That was a real obstacle, but if I wanted to continue writing I had to learn to tolerate it. Fatigue reared its ugly head too.

Following a year of prolonged writing and editing I suffered from back problems and shoulder pain. Those were a result of poor posture positioning as well as the physical task of using a keyboard. It became very debilitating, but there was no way I was going to allow it to stop me from finishing my book. It became a longer-term problem that I had to attend physiotherapy to address. I did exercises as directed, acquired support cushions for my work station and once again found a way to manage my adversity. It hadn't helped matters that my writing chair had been a soft sofa chair. Huge error on my part. I built up my stamina physically and mentally as I went on. I used sheer determination to power my way through when things got on top of me.

An extremely awkward impediment is the cognitive effects that too much conversation can have on me. That is a huge obstacle to everyday living and socialising. It is made worse when the verbal communication is fast or furious. If it's a situation where people talk over each other, I must bow out. Sometimes it feels like a train coming at me and whizzing by as I try to decipher and make sense of all the words. Other times, without any warning, I lose the thread of conversation. That, I find stressful. Loud voices and noises overwhelm me and I become fatigued as well as feeling the onset of what is referred to in MS as 'brain fog'. That is when the mind is overloaded and struggling for clarity and calmness. It is not the easiest subject to raise and certainly to direct people's speech and conversation is out of the question. You are likely to find me withdrawing or remaining uninvolved in some conversations. When I suggest I'd like a quiet life, I mean it literally. Closing my eyes at night can be the most anticipated respite from my day.

Sometimes it is not possible to find a way. A very rare occurrence, but still one I recognise the need to accept (still working on that!). Using public transport holds challenges for many people. For me, there may just be a few more. Buses are not kind to someone like me with balance and mobility issues. I have had doors shut on me as I was not quick enough to move off. That caused Elliot a great deal more stress than myself, who just got plain angry. I have lost count of the number of times I have missed my stop, despite ringing the bell as requested, because I did not make it to the front of the moving bus fast enough. It is a serious challenge to get to a seat before the bus thrusts forward taking the likes of me with it! After five long years of nursery and school bus journeys, I reached my limit. Elliot and I were travelling home with standing room only, as was common on the late afternoon route. As the bus erratically turned the corner, I was aggressively flung from one side to the other. I was clutching the school bag and jacket, which fell on the dirty floor as I desperately tried to grab hold of a support bar. I jerked my shoulder and neck, suddenly and violently, as the rest of the bus chatted and looked on. I could only then check if Elliot was all right. There he was standing firm, holding on, stressing about Mum again. Enough was enough. I instantly, without hesitation, said to him that it was his last ever school bus journey. His simple, but immediate response was 'Yeah!' Waiting in the cold and rain for an overcrowded bus to endure a bumpy and turbulent ride was not fun for anyone. But for me, it was dangerous, stressful and downright miserable. I decided there and then that we deserve better and made the clear decision we would use the local taxi service from that instant onwards. I somehow bent over, with the help of Elliot and the bar, to collect the items on the floor. No more holding on tight and hoping for the best! It was taxi time for the well-deserving Elliot and Mum. We had surely done our time on public transport. Five years we had stuck it out for. I had waited so long trying to cut costs, but some things are more important than money. My dignity for one. Elliot's anxiety the other.

There are no days without obstacles. There are no days without physical symptoms. Put them both together and there are no days I don't have to find a way around something or other. It can be frustrating and exhausting. It can also be uplifting and invigorating. Never more so than when I do find a way to achieve something that initially presented as too difficult. With so many obstacles and so much planning and alternative arranging to be done, it would be very easy to fall into the trap of feeling low or even overwhelmed. I think I could be excused for that, but it is just not in my make-up to feel or think that way. I make the best of everything. I find a way.

20

Cold Feet and Lead Legs

'It does not matter how slowly you go as long as you do not stop.'

(Confucius)

There is no greater challenge to me living my day-to-day life with MS than that of my cold and numb feet. That is very different from other challenges as it encompasses my whole being and has a lingering effect on everything I do and am faced with. From the very first day when my feet and lower legs started to go numb they have always been at the heart of my MS. During that first relapse I lost quite a bit of feeling in both feet, particularly my right. It goes without saying how much that would affect a person's life. So much of what you do requires your feet to assist you. The best way to describe it would be that there are areas with more feeling and areas with less or none. There is no pattern to this and it is impossible to be definitive. I could not for some time imagine how I could accept living with my feet this way. I absolutely hoped beyond hope the feeling would return. It never did and I have had to learn to live with it. After all they are my feet and I need them badly!

My feet are always cold and a constant reminder that I have MS, even during the more comfortable moments in life when all else feels well in and around my body. Not my feet. They always feel tight and restricted. The best description I have managed to come up with over the years is that my feet feel as though there are hundreds of little 'staples' all crushed and moving inside them. Sometimes they don't even feel attached to the rest of my body. Having my feet this way means different things at different times. It's not something I can focus on. That would bring me down and prevent me from getting on and doing day-to-day activities. I can't say for certain what the debilitating effect of my cold and numb feet is on my walking, but I'm pretty sure it's the main culprit with my disorderly gait. I've lost count of how many times I've bunglingly stood on Elliot's toes without realising! His kind understanding and tolerance are above and beyond. There are days it troubles me more than others, and sometimes when I close my eyes in bed I have the thought that I am looking forward to sleeping just to get some respite from my feet.

I have also had to make the transition from stylish heeled shoes to anything flat. I host an array of thick, usually grey, hiking socks that serve to try to heat the said feet up. They never match with anything and are not quite what I would choose. But hey, getting around and getting on are more the drivers than style and fashion these days. The circumstances around my feet are not something I give much attention to. It could easily dominate my life, but I took the decision very early on that I would not let it.

Further to all of this lies the issue that the rest of my undependable body does not respond well to the cold. It tends to stiffen up and living in a cold climate for way over half the year does create an issue for me. I just need to keep on the move where possible and avoid any length of time outdoors when it is very cold. Otherwise it is as though my legs need a reminder of what to do again. The stiffness prevents any fluid movements and it can be rather distressing. That tends to happen when I am standing or even sitting still for a few minutes. Once I start moving my legs loosen up and I can walk again, slowly. I should make the point that I always reach my destination despite the pace, despite the balance issues and despite the fact the rest of the world races past me. So, I think to myself, *does it matter?* I get there in the end. There are no alternatives so it is a matter of simply getting on with it. I do tend to stay indoors often in cold weather if I have a choice. I do have to brace myself as the season changes and get prepared for winter. It is far from ideal, but part of life for everyone.

There is also the perpetual issue of my legs and how they work daily. In the morning when I wake up it takes a few minutes to get an idea of how they are that day. On most days, they have a bit of energy and some reasonable movement first thing. What I do know and has changed very little since those early days is that they will deteriorate throughout the day. That is the case every day. It is undoubtedly a super challenging part of my life. The more bending and effort I require of them, the stiffer and heavier they become. And being a stay-at-home mum, who cooked every meal fresh, involved a lot of continuous movement that I didn't get much choice in. Especially during those baby and toddler years. It was constant, with the only exception being sometimes when I was on holiday resting and relaxing for most of the day. What I do know is by the end of our evening mealtime on most days, it is time for me to stop. It is with great relief normally I surrender to the need to rest my legs. That is why I only ever do something of an evening if it is essential. When I do dig deeper at such times, I have always surprised myself. But, I only do so if it is necessary.

Generally, I am aware of the need to rest so that I recover for the next part of the day or the following day. There is nothing more to it than I just need to stop. In the early days, I kept on going because Elliot was small and I wanted to prove to myself and others that I could do it. I don't feel that need anymore. Elliot is much more independent and I have proved myself over and over. We live and learn. On the other hand, sometimes this life doesn't allow for you to take things slower. I just need to adapt every single day and accept, hard as it may be, that there are tougher times than others. I have to live with my cold feet and lead legs. I have to incorporate them into everyday life. I am always trying to improve them and find a way for them to work better. I absolutely have not given up on that. In the meantime, I just need to keep going as best I can.

21

Goodbye to Shoe Heaven

'People don't change. Only their costumes do.'

(Gene Moore)

With the rather miserable issues centred on my feet, finding and wearing appropriate footwear has not been an easy task. That has been made even more difficult as I have always shared a great love of shoes since I was a teenager. Shoes and bags have been my favourite purchases. I never could resist a fabulous pair of shoes. From shopping trips in Covent Garden in London to Las Ramblas in Barcelona, I have tried and acquired every conceivable style and colour you could come up with! All that time and all those years I took for granted buying and wearing whatever shoes I wanted or liked. I have so many stories to share about my love of shoes and the journeys I have been on with all of them. But that's not for now. Instead I need to focus on what footwear I can walk safely in. That's a bit of a come-down, I have to tell you.

My last real encounter with a heeled shoe was my wedding day. I managed to wear them briefly after my CCSVI procedure, but I was quickly filled with fear and my movement was uncomfortably restricted. Whether I could have managed to wear them out and about I will never know. My fear of tripping and falling was too great and so I chose to abandon my attempts. I only tried on special occasions as flat shoes refused to give me the look I so desired. I cannot put into words how much I miss wearing fashionable high-heeled shoes. It may not seem important, but it has been to me. I have bought so many shoes and spent so much money on them. I have looked for vibrant colours and unusual designs. I have been constantly striving to replace the loss of that simple heel. I was always hoping that the next pair would be the ones. I have tried to add a bit of style or height, but without exception it has resulted in difficulties walking and I've had to abandon wearing each and every pair. All, that is, but one. I acquired a pair of knee-length red patent leather boots that fitted my requirements! They were comfortably flat, my insoles fitted in them, I could walk in them and I loved them!

I recall reading an article about a woman with MS who had taken the decision to use a walking stick as opposed to giving up heeled and fashionable shoes. She enjoyed a glamorous lifestyle up until her diagnosis and was damned that she should give that up. I felt nothing but admiration for her and still do. It would not have been the right decision for me and I didn't quite see myself dropping Elliot off in my stiletto heels at the school gate! My lifestyle was completely different, as was my personality.

I have had to accept the transition in my footwear and it has been a difficult process. It has taken me longer to accept that change, but I have done so in the end.

As time has gone on, I have become more focussed on walking safely than fashion. There were too many twisted ankles and accidents and so my sister has fallen heir to most of my shoes! There is one pair I bought for a friend's wedding some years ago that I keep in my wardrobe for nostalgic reasons! They were my all-time favourites and I still like to have them. I am not sure why, but I just do.

One of the falls happened in my living room from a mere standing position. I was wearing a pair of new trainers at the time. My foot just went over in them to the side very quickly. They were only one inch off the ground. It resulted in a rather painful and embarrassing black eye. I was relieved it happened during the school holidays as I could stay in the background until it was visibly better.

Following that accident, I decided to go to a store called Foot Solutions in Glasgow city centre. I had curiously passed by the shop a few times over the years. I was brave enough to venture in on one occasion in the early days, when I was relentlessly seeking support. The assistant with whom I spoke managed to put me off and I turned around and walked back out of the shop again. He showed me the types of shoes suitable for me at the time and foolishly thought it appropriate to point out the shoes that would be appropriate for me 'further down the line'. I made a choice not to ask or comment any further, but to just walk away. I do not have the energy to fight every battle. If I do not know what tomorrow is going to bring, how on earth someone else does is beyond me. No one knows what lies ahead or what may be around the corner. But once you have a diagnosis, I have found that some people think it is acceptable to make assumptions about you. It clearly is not acceptable. It is usually based on ill-informed information and more often than not, ignorance.

My walking was troublesome and combined with that fall, I decided to give Foot Solutions another chance. I made an appointment and had a full foot assessment, that time by a lovely professional and supportive assistant. It cost me several hundred pounds, but I eventually got shoes and individually made insoles to support my walking. They have indeed helped and I am now more focussed on the type of shoe I can wear. I still ask myself most days if that is my love affair with shoes over. Have I finally surrendered to the fact I cannot wear the shoes I like ever again? I think it is more accurate to say I want to feel safer and more stable and if what shoes I'm wearing determine that, then my choice is made. I keep an eye out for shoes that reflect who I am and not just the woman with MS.

I have twisted over in fashion sandals as well as falling flat on concrete wearing supportive sandals. I have fallen, as described, from a standing position wearing trainers. But my biggest and most scary fall happened barefoot and in my house, whilst standing still. From that I have learned there are no guarantees when it comes to the possibility of me falling over or losing my balance. What I am now much more aware of is that my choice of footwear can support me and reduce the risks. I am alert and concentrate on every step. That itself can be exhausting. I think it would be fair to say I am disappointed with the situation, but I have come to realise I should prioritise. It is obviously more important to stay safe than worry about what my footwear looks like. I can sometimes feel tired of always fighting and trying to overcome obstacles. Maybe there is a time and place just to remove them if it is possible. I have taken a lot of decisions and adapted many of my everyday experiences since being diagnosed with Multiple Sclerosis. That includes my footwear and it has asked a lot of me. I have done so thus far, even though it has involved a heavy heart on many of those occasions.

22

Motherhood

'There is nothing stronger in the world than gentleness.'
(Han Suyin)

Overcoming obstacles and accepting change, even when faced with tough transitions, has been fundamental over the years in allowing me to become and continue as an independent, able-bodied mum to Elliot. Being his mum is the most important thing in this entire journey. I am always striving to be the best mum I can. I would have tried to do that with or without MS. I had read and researched a great deal into parenting and child development long before MS came along. I had a lot of plans and ideas and very much wanted to raise Elliot as a fully active and involved mum. It mattered dearly to me to have boundless energy for the job and limitless patience to understand and allow him to flourish. Children are our greatest gift and deserve to be cared for with an abundance of love, endless understanding and immeasurable calmness. Multiple Sclerosis put up many barriers and made my quest profusely harder to achieve. But my commitment has remained the same and my determination never so much as faltered. If I have slipped up through the frustrations of MS and been impatient or agitated, then I have humbly apologised and refocussed myself to rise above my symptoms and prioritise Elliot's need. I am the first to admit I have made mistakes in motherhood, but I am the first to rectify them and take action to better myself and my parenting ability.

So much worried and unnerved me in the beginning about being a mum and looking after my own child. That was very much because of Elliot and MS being 'born together', giving me no time to come to terms with either. I had to 'hit the ground running' and often it was a case of muddling through the day. But I was in the beginning and still am certain I will never step aside and let anyone else do what would be often seen as 'mum's job'. Never. I will always be there, caring and nurturing Elliot first and foremost. Multiple Sclerosis will not take that from me. I will do everything humanly possible to be the one waiting on him with open arms at every point in his life.

Elliot was very mellow and calm as a newborn baby. He stayed like that for much of his infancy and was a real pleasure to be around. He was showered with attention from many and that seemed to be to his liking. As Elliot developed he was maybe not as mellow during those toddler years as he had been! He was exploring the world and met with some frustration along the way! That was disappointingly harder for me with MS. I needed much more energy and patience than I had. Not to mention my poor balance. The demands of a toddler are very high. On the days where I suffered acutely from fatigue, it was extremely tough to meet those demands. I was trying to cope with the symptoms of MS and at the same time juggling the varied calls of motherhood. It was not an easy balancing act. I don't think I got it right often enough. On so many days it was a case of struggling through. When I am under stress additional to my MS, it can be difficult to manage. Add into the mix a toddler and all his needs and you can have a tense situation. Elliot was too young to remember any of those occasions, but I do. I look back with real sadness at how my fatigue interfered with motherhood. I always will, but at the same time I have moved on and accepted that I did my best.

I looked for a little support and as usual did some online searching. I came across a publication called *The Happy Child Guide* by Canadian authors Blaise Ryan and Ashley Ryan. It was based around democratic ways to approach and deal with everyday, as well as the more difficult, scenarios attached to family life. I purchased the ebook and have followed their guidance and shared in their philosophy ever since. It is a very gentle way of parenting whereby you bring up your child without either bribes or punishments. It makes for a more peaceful family life and Elliot has responded very well indeed. Elliot began to mature and make excellent developmental progress. He has just prospered and loves home and family life with this very calm approach. There is always something out there to help you. You need to keep searching until you come across it. A happy child was exactly what I wanted and the more tools to help me, the better. Learning is another great gift in life. I believe emphatically as a person and especially as a parent your learning never stops.

When it came to Elliot's birthdays I just about managed to get away with a few people over at the house for the first few years. It was always challenging and came with some anxiety. That was somewhat disappointing, but in truth all parents can find parties, organising and entertaining stressful. I was the birthday boy's mum, so it came with the territory. As Elliot got a little older, he wanted parties with his friends. For me that meant I would have to experience exposure on the day. I was often dizzy, off balance and out of sorts. There were obstacles throughout the years: stairs, inclines, bright lights not to mention the screaming children! As with just about everything else with MS I wouldn't change a thing. Even with the challenges that were about, it was just a matter of finding a way around them. That has all just been part of being Elliot's mum and I have treasured every moment.

Over the years some of the most severe challenges to my ability as a mum came when Elliot was unwell. Such times are demanding of all parents. The difference being that I cannot ask MS to step aside. I have had to deal with them both. Those occasions were more hampering when Elliot was a baby and during his early years. It is not difficult to explain that sometimes as a mum you just have to give yourself over to caring solely for your child, especially if they are sick or at a time of greater need. On those occasions, there is no room for a disease like MS. You need to be able to cope with all that's going on. If you're having a 'bad leg' day, you simply cannot give into it and rest. It would be remiss of me not to say that I do get frustrated and disappointingly low on patience at such times. That's when I feel MS is bigger than me. As a parent, you cannot account for what life will throw at you without warning. On a day-to-day basis I have many things in place to help me cope. Sometimes however, life can put something down on your path to put you off-kilter. That does not make me different from other parents and carers. It can however make life overwhelming and on occasion it can feel too much to cope with MS on top of everything else. It is times like that where you will see me struggling somewhat. However, I will not allow myself to ever step aside and let anyone else look after Elliot when he is unwell, no matter how fatigued I am or what my mobility is like.

The first serious circumstance took place when Elliot was around sixteen months old. He was taken into Yorkhill's Royal Hospital for Sick Children in Glasgow with suspected meningitis. We were isolated in one room with our own toilet. I slept on a slim metal bed and Elliot was in his hospital cot. The pressure was huge and I got so little sleep. We both had cabin fever being stuck in one room all day and night with little contact from others. Visitors were allowed at certain times, but there was no contact on the ward otherwise. Trying to keep Elliot amused and settled was a never-ending battle. I will always remember him banging the metal bars of his cot in frustration. I did say previously that he has always been feisty! My lack of sleep over the four days alone had a huge impact on my MS, not to mention the stress and worry. I could not eat any of the food on offer due to my restricted diet, yet I was refused the use of the microwave as it was only for staff. I asked if a member of staff could place the food in the microwave and heat it on my behalf. My family were happy to prepare home-cooked food for me and bring it in. They refused once again. So, it was cold food or no food. I did eat, but it was the absolute minimum. Not the nicest of places I've ever stayed! My level of anxiety reached fever pitch. Elliot had a severe strain of a virus, not meningitis. He didn't quite recover from the ordeal for some time. He was traumatised by the invasive treatments and being caged in that tiny room for days. I shudder to think how we would have survived the experience without the *Noddy* DVD my sister found at the bottom of the ward's toy cabinet! It played on repeat on the small television screen we had in our room! We managed to get through the four days, but on our return home I wept with relief and exhaustion. Once again I had my own personal battle in front of me to climb back to some level of health and well-being. Arduous as it was, there was nothing else for it. All the time I still had to care and help Elliot recover, physically and emotionally. Hard times, but I was even harder.

Elliot was only three years old when he contracted the dreaded swine flu. You can but only imagine the upset and turmoil attached to that episode. The fallout was huge and lingered for many weeks. The house was turned upside down and there was so little sleep. The recovery process was long and hard. After that we didn't think life with motherhood and MS could get much more challenging, but Elliot came down with scarlet fever once he was at school. He couldn't eat or sleep; so no sleep for Mum or Dad then either. His staple diet was ice poles. I spent the days going in and out of consciousness and many symptoms flared up throughout my body. The upshot was weeks of turmoil and another long road to recovery. The relief when Elliot started to recover was so big as not only was he getting better and content again, but also it allowed me to even consider the MS side of life once more. Starting over became my norm and there was no room to grumble or reflect. Onwards and upwards every time.

That has been one of the most demanding parts of my journey to accept and come to terms with. I am normally so finely tuned and honed on my diet that my body struggled to cope when it was neglected. My body is programmed and keeps its strength and stamina through exercise and I rely so much on sleep and rest. When there is a deficiency in any of the above, I experience negative consequences. When there is the absence of all of them, I have a real uphill battle to recover. Fatigue spills over into my emotional health when I need to cope with extreme levels as I have done. With your energy drained it is almost impossible to think straight, never mind trying to walk straight. It was with great difficulty I started many days and I was not able to give any thought as to how I would get to the end of them. Each journey back was often not pretty and certainly not kind. It is an overwhelming factor of my motherhood and always will be. Although it gets easier as Elliot gets older.

I decided to give this 'condition' a name for Elliot when he was still very young. I wanted it to become a normal, natural and everyday thing. He was aware that I saw Dr Gilhooly to 'help' me and I always knew I would never leave it and build it into a bigger thing. My friend Liz told me once that she never remembers her mum and dad telling her she was adopted. She said they told her so young that she always just knew. That is what gave me the idea. I told Elliot to absolutely no reaction. His only comment was to ask 'but are you all right Mum?' That was a very normal response from a child needing comfort. I believe that being a parent is about giving children constant reassurance and so with that in mind, I went to great lengths to do so.

We play all the normal games and Mum does everything and more that Elliot would want of her. I do them differently and rather unconventionally, but I do them nonetheless. I always ensure that Elliot's life is full and enriched and make any arrangements necessary to provide that. Without exception, he has access to everything he requires despite there being limited mobility on my part. That is all made possible by the support on hand and there always being someone ready to take him wherever is required. It is normally Dad, but Aunty Maggie tends to make herself available with the car on the other occasions. A taxi is my last resort, but a reliable solution.

Motherhood has been a real pleasure for me regardless of having Multiple Sclerosis. I remain determined to aspire to whatever Elliot needs. That has been the focus of my self-help journey and the main reason I will continue prioritising my health needs. The greatest challenge ever presented to me was undeniably my son and Multiple Sclerosis being 'born together'. That took my journey with motherhood down a very different road. One with a lot more bumps and sharp corners. Both experiences would have been entirely different if they had come along on their own. But I will never know how things would have turned out. I have no desire to find out. Life is what it is, day by day. My unique journey has made me who I am and unquestionably shaped my relationship with motherhood.

I am blessed to be a mum. Truly blessed and forever grateful. MS has changed nothing of how I feel and what I want. It has only tried to change my ability to achieve those things. It hasn't succeeded. I have always found a way. Doesn't matter how deep you dig, I've learned there is always another layer you can reach to. There is no greater motivator than your own child. Elliot has no idea how powerful and inspirational he was and still is.

23

Acceptance

'Use what you've been through as fuel, believe in yourself and be unstoppable!'

(Yvonne Pierre)

I have long since considered all the different factors and changes MS has meant for me and my family. That has not been easy as it has meant facing up to a new reality. I had to accept the support that became necessary to my well-being and ability, particularly regarding Elliot, even though I am fiercely independent. I have had to battle with many obstacles and overturn them. I have had to come to terms with the loss of friends and diminished relationships. I have had to learn to live in a 'different' body. It just doesn't do what I ask it anymore. My life has changed beyond recognition in so many ways, but I am still the same old me underneath. My resolve has assisted me to accept the changes, but not accept I am a lesser person or should have to live a life of less quality. I have never once thought to myself *Why me?* Never. We are all equals in this life and no one knows what is around the corner. That is why it is essential to make the absolute best of whatever you have and don't wait until tomorrow to see if it brings something better. One day I could walk normally and the next day I could not. We are all only as good as we are on any given day.

The whole Multiple Sclerosis journey has been a very strange twist in my life. The consultant neurologist said that having a baby and the afterbirth process were the likely triggers for the onset of my MS. That resulted in the two being 'born together'. I am convinced that the stressful, traumatic birth contributed too as it is my belief that stress is an underlying part of many health issues. I have been able to accept all of that more easily because of having my precious Elliot. It is so complicated and emotional to think that the onset of Multiple Sclerosis had any relation to the birth of my wonderful son. It feels like it is by some twisted magic all of this happened. The most difficult and darkest thing in my life, Multiple Sclerosis, was in fact born out of the brightest and best thing in my life, Elliot. That really is life's greatest irony for me. What means a great deal is that I've never had any conflict over the two being 'born together' and coming into my life. If I were to choose to do it all over again, I would simply do the same thing. Elliot is a spectacular addition to my life and I am so content now I have him. Multiple Sclerosis is simply a by-product. I live as best I can and any negatives can never be compared to the positives and gains of having Elliot. He is simply terrific and I have a very full life with him and Allan. I know that fulfilment would not have been possible through any other means. I have no issue whatsoever with what happened to me. Life is full of twists and turns. My life has been one of two halves. The party girl travelling and teaching, who became a mum with Multiple Sclerosis. On paper the first half reads better, but in reality even with this disease the second half is most definitely the winner. I absolutely love Elliot to bits and the life I get to share with him.

I have found alternatives to the things I had to change and acknowledged there are some things I do not do anymore. I don't do stand-up aerobic exercises, go out much in the evenings or socialise with friends. The very small cluster that have remained are happy to make arrangements around my needs by meeting for lunch or afternoon catch-ups over a glass of wine. My best social events are pizza and prosecco around my kitchen table! Not forgetting I don't teach anymore either. I need to rest and withdraw when my body tells me to. I sometimes listen! Those sorts of changes are a direct result of MS. I can accept all of them because I have the whole magical world of Elliot. I am also privileged to have the relationship I have with Allan, which is full of love and fun. Having them both has more than made up for any loss. Adapting and accepting have allowed me to keep living an active and fulfilling life, undeterred by Multiple Sclerosis. That has been my key to living with this disease. I would not like to give the impression I have not felt loss and in those early days there was plenty of grieving. I also had a lot of fear and that is not something that has gone away. Having MS has made me much less likely to be spontaneous or go to places without Elliot or Allan. If I do, I will go with my sister Maggie. But having Elliot and becoming a small family unit has meant doing all sorts of other activities and trips. And the grass sure is greener on the other side. Life on this side with Elliot is better.

Not only has my life changed so much, but so has that of those closest to me. As well as devoting more of their time to support me, especially with Elliot, they have also had to emotionally come to terms with all the changes. We are a tight, small family where both Elliot and Allan have adapted and considered all my needs. My sister knows me as someone who initiates and organises, as well as being determined not to be limited. She doesn't think that me having MS has affected her life in any negative way whatsoever. She always responds whenever something is required, with or without notice. She is selflessly committed to supporting me. We share a good relationship that is notable for its laughter and positivity, even when presented with those testing times in life. The best therapy is love and laughter.

My mum found it very difficult to accept my diagnosis at first. She was distraught that I was coping with such extreme ill health at the same time as having my newborn baby. But life is all about perspective. I have shifted mine and see myself as differently abled, but able nevertheless. My mum has too. She has been around a great deal in Elliot's life, always on hand to look after him, especially in the baby and toddler years. She has 'walked' a lot of my MS journey with me. It was not a journey she ever wanted to be on, but one she has embraced in full regardless. Not just the anticipated difficulties, but also the many happy and positive times. We have laughed a lot more than we have cried. There is nothing we haven't found a way to do. Elliot has enlightened us every day. It has been a case of the half-full cup.

Acceptance seemed impossible at first. That was until I realised and began to own the fact it did not have to mean accepting a lesser quality of life. I cannot bring myself to accept I cannot do things. I must find another way no matter what I am confronted with. I will be like that for evermore. I surround myself with like-minded people who support my thinking and attitude. Together we have accepted my life has to be different, but together we have also established that is not a negative. Elliot is at the forefront of that.

It is imperative I point out the strain that having a chronic disease has put on my mental health, particularly in the early years. With all the obstacles and adversity, at times it was overwhelming. Acceptance has been an emotional rollercoaster. Never more so than when some physical improvement or temporary relief was too quickly followed by further exacerbation or indeed the return of my symptoms. All of that put immense pressure on me mentally and there were times I struggled to cope.

It would be misleading of me to give any impression that those times were either often or prolonged. As time has gone on you are likely to find me having a short outburst of frustration or venting my feelings and thoughts. What, on the other hand, is unlikely is that I would dwell on those feelings, repeat them or indeed make them the focus of my attention. I need all the energy I can get and so it is more than a rare occasion when you will find me wasting any. I don't ignore my thoughts and emotions, but I am very clear with myself there is nothing to gain by resting on negativity or going over things that have already happened.

It has always been in my nature to be resilient and determined. Even on the more trying days with this disease I have always believed and had hope that the next day could bring with it something better. Sometimes it has and sometimes it hasn't. I believe that the future still has an awful lot to give to myself and my family. I have not quite uncovered what that will be, but my mission to find it gathers momentum with each passing day. I will never give up. I will never give in to this disease.

I do look after my mental as well my physical health. Having such a great husband and friend as Allan contributes greatly. The whole wecanfindaway.com attitude, alongside the humour through good and bad times, has made the difference in allowing me to cope with everything. There is a very true saying sometimes that 'if you don't laugh, you'll cry'. I don't just hope that tomorrow will bring something better with it. I believe it will. Only ever accept the absolute minimum outside your control. I will not surrender to the low expectations that come from so many in relation to Multiple Sclerosis.

24

My Wife has MS

*'No relationship is all sunshine, but two people can share
one umbrella and survive the storm together.'*

(Unknown)

My husband, Allan, is central to this whole journey. He
has shared it all, from those first days of fatigue and early
signs of numbness. He watched in utter disbelief as his
wife's ability and strength crumbled in front of him. Not
only that, but it was running parallel to the birth and
bringing home of his newborn son. It was so obviously
difficult for me, but for Allan it was unfathomably tough.
He had all the physical stuff to address and shoulder
responsibility for. His son was days and weeks old and
his wife was deteriorating rapidly, without explanation.
It was so far-fetched, yet undeniably real. Allan also had
the commitment to his other son, Michael, who was
twelve years old at the time. Throughout everything
that happened, he never once missed seeing him. He
had the emotional strain, the worry and the fear of the
unknown. Allan had to present as strong and able, despite
his fear and doubts. There was no choice if he was to
cope with our newborn son on top of everything else

that was going on. He worked full time as a manager of a training organisation and his job involved travel and commitment. Allan couldn't get a single moment to himself to so much as recognise his feelings. It was simply a matter of ploughing on. We never talked it through. I was not well enough to take part in anything so we just carried on, whilst trying to convince ourselves everything would be fine. Allan held on for a long, long time to the fact that it was all linked to the caesarean and difficult birth. He felt the timing was too incredulous not to be. Allan has been the greatest support and strength possible.

Allan wanted to keep things similar to the way we already lived and planned to bring up Elliot. He accepts MS as just another thing in life, amongst the many we have to deal with. He is thoroughly disappointed that this is something in life he can't fix, but at the same time he will carry on making the best of everything. Where he differs is that he feels exceptionally let down by our NHS here in the UK. It is important to stress that he is not referring to all the services we have been in contact with. However, Allan has felt since the early investigations into my symptoms and the clumsy way I discovered my diagnosis that things have been laden with problems. He believed the level of care given to me with a chronic condition was very poor and found that frustrating, as well as hugely disappointing. He admits he lived under the illusion that if you were diagnosed with a chronic condition, you would then be under medical supervision and guidance for the long term. I, on the other hand, have received care that at best could be described as patchy. It was very basic and considering my diagnosis of a lifetime chronic condition, it was for the shortest of periods. It was not holistic care and the hospital had no interest in my alternative and complementary approach. They did not attempt to offer any long-term plan to improve my health. Due to my wish not to take any of the drugs available, and with good reason, I was discharged. I was given the final say, but it is not difficult to determine if I jumped or if I was pushed.

Allan feels strongly that any doctors who try to break new ground with treatments are put down by the General Medical Council (GMC). People like me are left to our own resources to deal with our condition, as doctors who try to be pioneering and progressive are hampered and restricted. There is so little on offer on the NHS and almost no funding for new treatments. Many people find themselves not well enough or without sufficient support to cope. I am fortunate to have my wonderful husband and friend Allan. However, neither of us realised how poor long-term care was here in the UK. It is not necessarily a reflection on the hard-working NHS staff or its aims to care for people, but more likely down to finance. But it does mean you have a better chance of a decent quality of life if you are privileged enough to have good support along with your own determination.

Allan is like me in that he does not look very far into the future. He did not choose to do so before my diagnosis and therefore where would be the logic in doing so now? He would describe himself firmly as a pragmatist and as such just gets on with things and lives with whatever is put down on his path. Allan has taken my diagnosis 'on the chin' and shares very much in my onwards and upwards attitude. I know it has hurt him a lot and he always wants to help and manage our adversity. He always puts himself out and puts himself last. He sometimes struggles because I demand to be so independent all the time, but I will never step back and be vulnerable. The only thing Allan indulges in outside the family is any form of sport, from local ones to all American sports. There is no exception to that, but there is emphasis on football. That is his bit of escapism. He goes to football league matches and follows rugby here in Glasgow as and when he can. Elliot is right behind him these days. It takes him out of our much-cluttered world of challenge and often intensity. It works for him and I am relieved he has something to escape to.

We lost our way as husband and wife a little during those first frantic couple of years. It was not in a negative way, but simply because we had to contend with so much. We were the strongest of teams, but we had barely stopped to look upwards as we laboured on through our stormy life. Elliot demanded so much of our attention, which we happily delivered, and Multiple Sclerosis followed a very unpredictable course. It was almost impossible to get any time to ourselves. When we did manage to catch a minute we were both too tired to talk about anything of substance, never mind being able to do anything! Allan was determined we would manage together. We both shared looking after Elliot. Allan was also coping with the pressures of his working life too. It was a great deal to live with. I think you could say it was sheer bloody-mindedness that got us through. Individually we do not respond to calls to stop and that we have reached our limit. When we join forces, we are formidable.

I had most definitely drifted away in my struggle to get on top of my debilitating symptoms. I was uncomfortably obsessed by MS and any other time left was devoted uncompromisingly to Elliot. Being a parent means you have so many different things to deal with and once you add to that Multiple Sclerosis and its temperamental course the pressure starts to build on you and your family. That would be true of our situation. I had unintentionally forgot that I was still a wife and friend to Allan. With the greatest love and respect in the world, Allan had slipped off my radar on a day-to-day basis. It was purely about survival and getting through each day. There was nothing I could do to change that. We had been so excited awaiting the birth of our baby. It was overwhelming when he arrived and almost immediately I was so unwell and struggling to walk independently. It was a great deal for both of us to withstand and we were under a lot of stress and pressure. Individually we found ways of coping on a day-to-day basis. I couldn't love Allan any more, but at the same time I couldn't give him any more. He had to be stronger than imaginable and cope with everything. I have so much admiration for him. He has never so much as flinched in this whole journey. Not a moan or groan. Plenty of expletives, but that is Allan's style! A short outburst and then dig even deeper.

After around two years we decided to try and get some time for ourselves as a couple. It had been a long two years where so much happened, but we knew it was time to stop and step outside of the intense cloud we were living under. It was time to just be husband and wife again. We planned a short break away for just the two of us. I was far enough along my self-help journey to be well enough to go. We liked to let our hair down in the past when the occasion allowed, but it was all a bit unknown now I had Multiple Sclerosis. So many changes had happened and I wasn't sure if the old Tricia had gone away altogether. I wouldn't have blamed her if she had.

I could only agree to one night away from Elliot. That would be long enough for me – and Allan for that matter. It had been quite some time since we had spent more than a baby-sitting night together as a couple. Those were few and far between when Elliot was a baby. The first year of his life had been a case of managing our circumstances. The next year I had been caught up with my self-help journey, trying to bring myself back to some state of health and ability. The time for a little trip away felt right. We chose to go to the lovely Hotel du Vin near the centre of Edinburgh. Elliot stayed with his Aunty Maggie. I was looking forward to a little time to ourselves and just stopping for a while. We travelled by train and taxi. It was a relatively easy journey and did not demand a lot of me physically. Edinburgh is a great city. It is far quirkier than many other cities and always hosts that little bit of something alternative. On our arrival, it was a fabulous hotel and room in a super location. We were very happy and a little eager. I was benefiting immediately from a restful day with virtually no walking or mobility requirements. Being over-excited we ventured out almost straightaway and had lunch in the Elephant House Café where JK Rowling is suggested to have written parts of the early Harry Potter book. The whole area had a real buzz about it and that just added to the way we were feeling!

There were plenty of lovely places on our doorstep and so it required very little of my mobility. We returned to the hotel to relax before dinner. The first thing we would normally do would be to open some wine. Things were different now. I couldn't drink very much anymore and my walking wasn't good to start with. I would still have a glass of wine, but usually at home and always controlled. *But then again*, I thought, *old habits die hard!* There was no question of deserving it. Allan was delighted. The old Tricia was still about. The wine was dutifully uncorked!

We chilled out, had a cava and later went for dinner in the hotel. It was a fabulous meal and when Allan ordered champagne I knew I was in trouble! I think we were both over-excited! The term 'you don't get out much' surely applied to us! The restaurant met all my dietary requirements and that felt good. We had lots of laughter and what could only be described as carry on. We chose not to mention anything serious and managed to forget our entire goings-on for that one evening, except for text messages to check on Elliot. After dinner and that champagne, I had to make my way from the restroom to Allan in the bar area. He was on a mission by now and whisky was his next victim! At the door of the bar I thought to myself that I wasn't going to make it across the floor. I centred myself and took three or four strides to land just about where Allan was sitting! I got there and that time indulged in some sparkling water!

We had great fun and it felt good. The old Tricia was still in there and came out to play! She had been away for quite a while, but it was good to know she could come back. Allan, on the other hand, had just been soaking up the pressure and that was his first opportunity to let some of it go. He was not obliged to limit his intake of alcohol as I was, so he didn't! As a couple, we still had our old spirit and were still the best companions. I had a little more wine than would be advised, but enough for it all to be fun. I was worried that because there were restrictions on me, regarding my mobility and fatigue, our trip away would be unrecognisable. I did not need to worry. It was such a refreshing and energising time. Allan and I were still the same old us. We both went home happy. It is imperative whilst surrounded by my medical condition that I do not let it become or define who I am. On the evidence of that trip, it is unlikely.

We have been away for several trips since. It is our little respite time. We try to go away at least once a year for an overnight. We never go too far and it's just an opportunity to unwind and recharge from our daily life. We always enjoy it and it keeps just a tiny piece of our lives where it's just husband and wife time. Elliot does not come with us and MS is most certainly not invited.

Allan's life changed the day Elliot was born forever, but not simply for the reasons you would ordinarily associate with fatherhood. His wife got MS too, but he has adapted without question or hesitation on every occasion and for any reason. He is strong, dedicated and determined. We share our journey, our sense of humour and our unbreakable spirit.

25

My Mum has MS

'Love is when he gives you a piece of your soul, that you never knew was missing.'

(Torquato Tasso)

Elliot is a very special boy in so many ways. What may be adversity to others is very much his 'normal'. He has never known his mum to be any other way than his mum with MS. He is super-resilient and adaptable. He is a very emotional young boy who wears his heart on his sleeve. He is unusually comfortable expressing himself for a child of his years. He is very inclusive and thinks so much about other people's needs. He shares the same strive for fairness and equality that both Allan and I have.

Elliot is aware that I alter how things are done both at home and outdoors. He has had to make sense of that in his own little world. I can see that he has grown up taking it in his stride. He is a very strong-willed and determined young boy and always has been. They are fine attributes and will take him a long way in life. I still must take great care to protect him and make sure he is not exposed to any negativity that may be attached to my MS, although that has become less and less of an issue as he has got older.

Elliot did not have much understanding of my mobility issues in the early years and so he would get more than a little flustered when we missed the bus or my balance was tested as the bus surged forward. He was unfazed by my physical appearance and mobility, but found it hard to understand why Mum never managed to catch the bus. I found it even harder to explain. We just got on with life no matter what, always side by side. When we were out and about travelling, or going to and from nursery, it was difficult to know what to do for the best. It was all uncharted territory. I was acting on my instincts and trying to make the right choices. With hindsight, maybe I should have been more honest and explained to Elliot what was hindering me. Then again, he was so young and I was trying to protect him.

As time moved on and Elliot grew up he started to realise there was difficulty with my walking and mobility. We decided we would take it much slower. We got very wet, waited long periods on buses and got so cold at times on our journeys. I recall one day battling our way against the wind and rain. There were huge hailstones whacking off our faces. Elliot shouted 'We're under attack, Mum!' I had to tell him it was just an ordinary day here in Scotland! A taxi would be required some days down to school. On a particularly troublesome day with fatigue or balance, a taxi would be required for the pick-up at the end of the day too. For many years I juggled between the bus and the taxi for the school run. There are so many memories of those times. It was just Elliot and Mum times. We coped together! I'm simply Mum to Elliot and although I had my personal challenges going on, we did all the regular things hand in hand.

I have always made a point to talk to Elliot about his thoughts and feelings. Over the years he has gradually become more familiar with the things that Mum will be able to do and those she will not. He has become more likely to turn to Dad for certain things as time has gone on. Elliot is aware some games are off the menu when Mum is involved. He is able to be grown up about it for the most part. On the other hand, he was just a young boy and sometimes wanted everything! That's when he would suggest I went in goal during football in the garden! Refereeing from a sitting position was his last resort! He certainly understands that his mum is 'differently' abled at times. I'm very clear he should tell grown-ups his worries and always feel safe and secure. I devote much of my life to him feeling that way.

Elliot did once say to me that 'MS makes you trip and it's a bit scary'. He added that it was only sometimes, but it made him worry. All I can keep doing is my very best and give him as much confidence as possible. I find it a bit scary too at times. On an exceptionally positive note he passed a comment entirely out of the blue one afternoon. He casually said to me, 'Mum, do you know the way you wobble about and your balance is funny?' I replied simply with 'Yes.' He continued, 'That's like your trademark.' He went on to say that I just wouldn't be me any other way. That was indeed my finest ever compliment and certainly is the way to include people and celebrate difference. I couldn't ask for Elliot to be any more wonderful than he is.

As much as I am his mum, Elliot is my son. He has always been kind, considerate and gone out of his way to care. We share a very close bond and one of our most treasured experiences together happened one Saturday afternoon in early autumn, when Elliot was only five years old. We had gone to visit a great place called The Burrell Collection over in the south side of Glasgow. We spent the first part of our trip inside the museum and it was not long until Elliot became excited to get to the park. My sister headed to the café to get refreshments and we went in the other direction. Elliot and I were chatting together as we meandered through the lovely country park. More accurately, Elliot strolled across the grass and I bounced from side to side as always! He was such good company and invariably had a story to tell. There was never a silence when you were with Elliot.

Elliot let go of my hand and he was off. There was plenty for him to do and I wandered somewhere behind, following his trail and keeping a mindful eye on him. He would make his way over to me every now and again. On one occasion, he asked if I would go with him to the rope slide to help him mount it and give him a push. Off we went in that direction and made our way up the small incline. It was a grass verge with some ten steps. They were long and wide steps, just sitting on their own with no railing or supports either side. As always with those types of things, hand in hand Elliot and I went up. I took each step cautiously and was not at all confident in doing so. However, without any great thought I went up them with Elliot's hand to help balance me. I gave no consideration to how I would descend the small hill. If I stopped and thought about such matters I would seldom go ahead in the first instance. He proceeded to have a few turns on the slide. I was not the best at helping him jump on it. Neither am I particularly strong to give a good push off or steady on my feet. I gave it my best shot. Elliot met another boy and they started to chat. The next thing I knew Elliot was off and running with his new friend back down to the other activities around the park! I watched him running across the park, looked around and thought to myself that I was in fact 'stranded' at the top of the little hill!

There was no way I was getting down those steps with nothing to hold onto. I did not consider for one second negotiating the grassy hill. It would have been one step, two steps and down I go! So there I was, stuck up such a small incline with no real option of getting down without fuss or help. I looked a bit strange standing there without my child nearby. I got to some quick thinking. Option one was to ask someone to take my arm and help me down. Mmmm, that was not presenting as a comfortable option. The alternative was to slide or bump down. Now based on the wecanfindaway.com approach to life, that looked the more likely candidate. Fiercely independent as I was it would get me back down on flat ground again and that after all was the object! I was in a park across the other side of the city from where I lived so I didn't know anyone in case I felt awkward.

I looked around before deciding on the best moment to bump down. I noticed Elliot a little in the distance. He looked up and saw me and without a moment's hesitation, he just ran towards me and up the hill. He did not say a word. He just reached out his hand and I took it. Slowly and a little wobbly, we descended the steps. I felt huge relief that I was back down on flat ground again. He let go of my hand and ran off as fast as he had come over. He went straight back to playing with his friend. He shouted a vague 'Bye Mum' as he ran away, but we never spoke another word about it. That was not in line with the close relationship Elliot and I shared. But for some reason we both knew just to leave it there. I felt overwhelmed with love and care, despite not a word having been spoken. My sister arrived with my green tea completely unaware of what had just happened. I chose not to share the story at the time as I felt such deep emotion about it. It was a special moment between Elliot and me.

Elliot never asked why I was still up the hill or if I needed help. Somehow at the tender age of five he instinctively knew what to do. He did it with no fuss and I just love him for being like that. That just highlights who Elliot is. He cares, he helps and he looks after. He has extraordinary mature and developed awareness as well as strong empathy for his young years.

Elliot's mum has MS and she has had to adapt, but she has done so with energy and positivity. Elliot has responded equally as enthusiastically, whilst displaying understanding and great loyalty. They have both enjoyed their journey together and there have been far more positives than negatives. Life has been abundant with happy memories and experiences. Multiple Sclerosis has not dampened their spirits and Elliot has been brought up in the understanding that life is not about problems, but about finding solutions. Celebrate difference and you will have a wonderful life celebrating.

26

Travelling

'If you don't like something, change it; if you can't change it, change the way you think about it.'

(Mary Engelbreit)

Learning to celebrate difference taught Elliot from a very early age to adapt and think about how to include everyone and meet differing needs. That is something we would all like our children to do, but it has become second nature to Elliot. In my life, it is applicable to most things and none more so than holidays and trips.

It was always going to be difficult with MS to go to some destinations. I was constantly worrying about what the future would hold and about Elliot having the same opportunities, despite Multiple Sclerosis. It consumed me. So many facilities and parks for families involve walking and being on your feet for long periods. That, of course, is the area where I have a great deal of difficulty and so it would affect just about everywhere we would wish to go.

Elliot's first trip with the nursery presented my first challenge, but it was essential he should not miss out because his mum had MS. I was not comfortable asking

Allan or anyone else to go in my place. It was a day trip to Louden Castle theme park in Ayrshire. As the day went on, my legs got heavier and heavier. They also got stiffer and lacked power. I kept going, but it was with difficulty. It is a little complex to explain, but it brought with it a strain I did not mind. The pleasure of being a mum and sharing Elliot's joy and experience overtook anything else that was going on. Love and persistence got me through. Thankfully it was all on the bus for two o'clock in the afternoon. I was still smiling as Elliot had enjoyed his day thoroughly. I had spent most of it with one of the other mums, Debbie, who always made life easier with her laidback and accommodating way. She did not, then or since, comment on my walking and balance. In fact, she has never so much as looked down at my legs as they struggled to get me from A to B! That is something that ordinarily comes with the territory of being 'differently' abled. Most people cannot help themselves as their eyes are drawn to my legs. I am constantly and disappointingly stared at. But not with Debbie and I am so grateful we became friends. Her support and inclusive, respecting attitude over the years have been invaluable to me.

It would be impossible to imagine not being part of precious trips like that with my child. I remember so much detail from that day because I had to think through every step I took. It is amazing how many people take a day like that for granted. They are not granted to everyone. I regard any experience like that one so highly. Put simply, I can't take them for granted. That was to be the first of many of those days as Elliot had reached the age for theme parks.

Soon after that Elliot wanted to go to Disneyland. That was going to be my biggest test with MS, but I would do everything I could to make it happen. A huge amount of planning went into our trip to Paris. As with other theme park visits, my legs got heavier and stiffer throughout the day, so we retired to our comfortable hotel room for a rest mid-afternoon. I did make a special effort to go to Mickey's Café on one of the nights. I still have vivid and great memories of that night, making it worth the extra push needed to get myself there and back after a day in the theme park. I walked arm in arm with Allan to let him take the strain of my balance issues by that point in the day. Elliot ate just about nothing of the most expensive meal he's ever been bought! Dairy free and low saturated fat diets do not exist in Disneyland so it was another hungry night for me! But at only four years old, Elliot fought with the 'real' Captain Hook and hugged Mickey himself! Memories to treasure! I am so pleased and proud I took him on trips like that when I did. It is another example of why we need to seize the moment and every day.

Having outgrown Mickey and friends at a young age (thankfully!), Elliot turned his attention to Lego once he was at school. He set his sights on Legoland! My unpredictable walking was not at its best the year we decided to go. Another trip to a huge theme park did not fill me with great anticipation. I knew I would need a big improvement before we were due to go. It is difficult to measure the changes in my mobility throughout the years. Suffice to say that I have to keep working harder and harder to be able to do and achieve things that may have been previously within my reach. I made a firm plan to prepare myself for the trip. As always that meant a strong focus on my food and drink intake as well as increasing my gym visits. I spent months sourcing better footwear. I gave it my best shot to make sure that Elliot could enjoy the full experience, despite his mum's wavering ability. The planning, as always, was meticulous and arrangements were made to alleviate as many foreseeable issues as possible. That is not the usual planning that would go into a holiday or short break, but it has been since I have had Multiple Sclerosis. It has allowed me to achieve what may otherwise have been unachievable.

We flew down to London and stayed at an airport hotel, arranging to travel to Legoland in the morning. That was the first big mistake in my planning as Elliot jumped in the air at 4.20 am asking if it was time to go yet! He stayed awake asking the same question over and over until we set off! Our arrival at the Legoland Hotel was the best memory of the entire trip! Elliot was about to combust with excitement and let out a yell as the taxi turned the corner and there stood a colourful, life-sized Lego brick construction that we were going to sleep in! Finding out part of the park was set on a hill was not the most inspiring news to arrive to. Maybe the name Hill Top Café in the brochure should have given me a clue! All that planning and I hadn't picked up on that information. Nonetheless that wasn't going to change any time soon and so it was time to plan the day as best we could. Although my mood did dip a little with that discovery, I didn't let on. It was only part of the park and we would visit it once on each day. I would do my best to manage.

Elliot was in his element and I had the security of always being a short distance away from our room and a rest! That is the reason we booked to stay in the resort. It may have been more expensive, but it was worth it to eliminate the additional travel and mobility challenges of a hotel further afield. I learned that from our Disneyland experience. That has become an integral part of all my plans and journeys over the years. I always book the most convenient, comfortable and accessible option. Without exception that has incurred higher costs. There is a straightforward choice. If we cannot afford the one that is most suitable to my needs, then we do not go. That applies to everything across the board. Elliot has benefited from some fine hotels and holidays in his short life! Mum having MS has meant a big upgrade on hotels, travel and resorts!

The fun-filled park was well laid out with lots of resting places and quieter areas to recoup. There were plenty of railings for support. To our great relief there was a train ride up the hill with the super café and resting spot at the top to recharge for the rest of the day. They even sold healthy, high protein vegan foods! An enormously welcome surprise. We didn't find the train stop on the first afternoon so I clambered all the way up the hill! I should add that just a glance at Elliot's excited face always gave me the extra surge I needed. I tried to make it as good as possible for Elliot, with minimal stress and worry for Allan. As we climbed the mobile stairway, with the sun shining, onto the aeroplane back to Glasgow I did look back with a smile and indulge in a tiny moment of 'Yes, I've done it again' under my breath!

Life had changed so much for us that we considered carefully where else we could go. Backpacking trips with our *Lonely Planet Guide* were over. We needed a bit of confidence and security to support us. We regularly travelled around Scotland, but decided to try some holidays abroad. Weekends at theme parks were great fun, but we were hoping to relax more and maybe indulge in some warmer weather. I tended to react to heat as is very common with MS and so I had to be careful. The first throws of spring in Spain suited us fine as the temperature was still in the early twenties, but once Elliot started school we were forced down the route of travelling at high season. That increased our costs firstly, but also brought with it the issue of hotter weather. That presents huge barriers when you have MS as heat can bring on symptoms. We went to our own villa on one occasion where I managed relatively well considering the July sunshine. That was mostly due to having our own pool as a cooling-down method throughout the day. We also didn't stray too far from the air-conditioned villa as that left me drained and 'not fit for purpose'. The hired car had to come everywhere with us and we spent most of our time at the villa.

It was the first evening of that holiday, only hours after settling into our villa. I had just helped prepare dinner and whilst walking on the concrete patio to the dining table outside, I somehow tripped. I was carrying plates and with my hands full there was nothing to break my fall. I very aggressively landed straight onto my knees. The family gasped as I hit the concrete and the plates smashed in different directions. It was excruciatingly painful and took some assistance to get me back onto my feet. The fall took my breath away. We had to wait at first to see if there was any damage that required medical intervention. Not too long passed and we felt confident enough I had been bashed and bruised, but it was not more serious. That fall was simply due to wearing summer sandals, something rarely associated with life back home and so I was not familiar with walking in them. On what was nothing more than one of my 'regular' stumbles, the sandals just did not support me. Not to mention the fact that being my over-ambitious and invincible self I had not left a hand free to support any such stumble! What were to develop over the coming hours were two huge bruises, one on each knee. For the rest of the holiday I had to walk around with those large bruises changing colour day by day! In the scheme of Multiple Sclerosis, it didn't dent me. I limped around for the first couple of days after the fall and undoubtedly my pride was hurt. I almost tried to ignore the fact that it happened as I was uncomfortably embarrassed. As for the physical bruises, well, they faded soon after being back on home soil.

We did try one more annual holiday overseas, just off mainland Spain. We opted for a hotel to get more rest and for convenience. Not my best decision. The temperature soared, making it unbearably hot every day in the July sunshine. I would react and become listless and weak. That affected almost everything we tried to do. I did not have the opportunity or physical ability to dip in and out of the busy hotel pool, which was not easily accessed. That minor detail made all the difference. The hotel was large and covered a lot of ground, which meant there was a great deal of walking on my part. I was a combination of agitated and disappointed. Not to mention all washed out. To top it off, as a vegetarian in Spain my food selection at the hotel was somewhat restricted to say the least. I was very uncomfortable eating foods for which I did not know the fat content as I knew it could have an adverse effect on me. Half a stone lighter, I arrived home. I was weak, unrested and fatigued. On our return, we decided we would try a staycation next time.

The following year I chose a cottage in south Wales. It was part of a unique set-up of renovated cottages, playing fields and an outdoor pool. There was an enormous amount of space for everyone and best of all Little Loveston was flat for the most part. We picked a year with great British weather, but not too hot. It was sunny every day with the temperature in the early twenties. Day trips to the beach were easily accessible. There were plenty of healthy food options at the farm shop, only yards from the cottage, and a big dining kitchen to cook and indulge in. That was the first family holiday where I did not have a reaction to the heat, a poor diet or indeed the physical layout of the place. All my research had at last paid off! I was not the only satisfied customer. Elliot was full of its praises as were Allan and the rest of my family who were holidaying with us. I do not think we will venture further afield for some time. I recognise after years of searching that self-catering options are most definitely better suited to my health and well-being. I have been fortunate enough to have travelled to my satisfaction prior to MS restrictions being applied!

It can be a stressful event for me to plan and pay for a holiday not knowing if it will be suitable. I have had more than my fair share of let-downs. We do return to places we are familiar with and that are appropriate when we can. We are extremely fortunate here in the United Kingdom to have so many great places to go. Scotland is spectacular itself. The relief of enjoying something as simple as a holiday and being a full participant throughout instead of feeling washed out and with zero energy was overdue. Maybe it was something I wrestled with for longer than I should have? Maybe I did not meet my usual high standards of accepting and adapting? Maybe I was not pleased at feeling like my choices were limited? Maybe I believed that going abroad would compensate Allan and Elliot for the negatives I had brought to their lives because of Multiple Sclerosis? I think I did struggle more with that one and trying to meet other people's needs. I also think I got it wrong. Whatever the case, the lessons have been well and truly learned.

Travelling on both long and short trips, home and away, have brought with them a mountain of obstacles and complexity. I have immersed myself in them all and learned a great deal from the many experiences. It was more fun and fulfilling to push the boundaries and not accept those invisible restrictions. I was determined that Elliot would not be limited in any way by Multiple Sclerosis. There have been immense rewards in managing all our trips and it has been somewhat exhilarating despite the challenges. We need to remember what we have got and what we can achieve. The human soul knows no bounds. We put restrictions on ourselves and we must get better at lifting them and going for what we want. Planning and preparation are key. Once they are in place with some hard work and determination, people could astound themselves with what they are capable of. Sometimes it is our head that holds us back, telling us we can't or shouldn't do something. Luckily, I've never listened much to my head, I've always just gone with my heart.

27

Discrimination

'I believe discrimination still exists in society and we must fight it in every form.'

(Andrew Cuomo)

Difficult situations and obstacles have come in many forms over the years. None have been more challenging than those that have evolved from unwelcome outside interference. I have been and am judged far too often by what people see and their first impressions. That is in fact discrimination, even though many people tend not to see it that way.

The most extreme discrimination happened in a grocery shop when Elliot was seven years old. It was one of the leading supermarket's smaller city centre stores. I had been for Sunday lunch with Elliot, my brother Ricky and his nine-year-old daughter, Helena. I had enjoyed a small glass of wine with my pizza. We were being picked up in the car by my sister and so I decided to buy a couple of items. One of which was a small 187 ml bottle of prosecco to take to Gran's as we were stopping by for a visit on the way home. My brother was served first and to give you some background to the situation, he too had enjoyed a glass of wine with his lunch a little earlier. He was served by the checkout assistant and his shopping basket included wine, which he was sold without any issue. Why would there be? Everything seemed fine at that point. I was next to be served and almost immediately I sensed something was not quite right. The frowning shop assistant was female and young. She scanned my first couple of items and then abruptly stopped. Without warning, she looked at me and sharply asked, 'Have you been drinking?' She had in her hand the small bottle of prosecco. I was shocked and taken aback. I replied awkwardly that I had a small glass of wine with my lunch two hours ago. I could not believe I had to answer such a question in a public forum or that I felt it necessary to emphasise it was a small glass. I very reluctantly went on to explain I had Multiple Sclerosis and that is why she may have seen me somewhat 'off balance'. Having to announce that to a stranger in front of a queue of people was not something I was very happy about at all. My words were floundering and hesitant. By now Elliot was getting worried and agitated and I thought it would be best to try and divert the situation. I was entirely unsuccessful as the shop assistant responded, 'I can smell drink from you.' I was stunned at her reaction. She went on to state, 'I can't sell you this wine.'

I had reached my forties and was allowed a glass of wine. Yet that young shop assistant thought she had the right to challenge and attempt to humiliate me because I had balance issues. She had overstepped the mark. I was extremely upset and therefore my reply was not instantaneous. My words when they did arrive were to retort with the same explanation I had been forced into giving moments earlier, that I had a small glass of wine with my lunch. I pointed out that it was an acceptable thing to have done and she had no problem serving my brother, who too had enjoyed a glass of wine with lunch.

I was in no way under the influence of alcohol and was simply having a family Sunday lunch out with one small glass of wine. Something I rarely allowed myself to do, but I had decided on that day to relax my strict rules about wine consumption. Lunch out with my brother was not exactly a regular thing and that one small glass of wine was in fact me 'letting my hair down'. Nothing seemed to make any difference to the shop assistant's attitude, which was at best condescending and at worst insulting. I reiterated for the last time about having MS, once again to no avail. Elliot was by that point upset, but I took the decision to confront the situation.

I did stop and explain to Elliot that Mum was all right and the lady was in the wrong. I asked him to wait outside with my brother as I had called for the manager. They were not willing to leave me in the shop by myself. My brother pointed out to the shop assistant that she was being very unreasonable and displayed a poor attitude. That made no difference and there was no doubt in my mind she had made a judgement that I was under the influence of alcohol with my young son. The only reason she came to that conclusion was because my balance was off, as it was every day of my life, due to the fact I have Multiple Sclerosis. It does not take much to work out she was in fact discriminating against me. Not the first and not the last time that has happened. It was however very public on that occasion and delivered with a derogatory attitude.

The manager arrived smiling. He was young and male, appearing awkward from the beginning. I explained the situation and how I had been treated by one of his shop assistants. I told him directly about her shocking attitude and how I was spoken to in front of all the other customers in the shop. I informed him of my condition and once again had to make public that I had a glass of wine with my lunch. I went on to point out that anyone else in the shop seemed to be allowed to do that, but because I have a chronic disease which affects my balance I am not to be afforded that privilege? He sent the shop assistant off the shop floor, but upheld her decision. She was almost smiling as she left, seeming rather pleased with her disruptive efforts. He did apologise that it had all happened and agreed to sell the minuscule bottle of wine to my brother.

I had made my points at length, with a seven-year-old Elliot adding that his mum had Multiple Sclerosis and 'it's not her fault'. I decided as the manager had conceded and I had the wine in my possession, we would leave the store. Just before we did I took the time to ask if he was confident of his decision as it would certainly not be the last time he would hear from my good self. Even though he was reluctant he still gestured that his decision would remain. We all left visibly upset and shocked. Shop workers should be trained in the sale of alcohol and the laws that surround it as well as discrimination matters. The shop assistant thought she knew what she was doing, but I was determined to prove she did not. It would not be an understatement to say I was incandescent.

On the car journey home, I concentrated on Elliot and explained clearly what had happened. At no point in the shop did I raise my voice or be rude, but I was on the other hand very assertive and to the point. I explained that sometimes you should walk away from a situation and other times you need to stay and defend your position. That growing up in life would help him learn which times were for what. I cuddled him and asked if he could try to understand this was an occasion I had to stand up. It was complex stuff for a youngster, but necessary too. It was the first occasion since having MS and being a mum I had allowed the focus to be my needs, if only for a few minutes. To this day, I still believe it was the correct decision not to simply walk away. I had no intention of leaving the matter there and planned to take it to its rightful conclusion.

On our return to the house I telephoned the headquarters of the store and spoke to the customer services department. Only to be met with yet another employee with no understanding of either discrimination law or indeed licensing law. He responded by suggesting that the assistant only questioned me because I had admitted having a glass of wine with my lunch. He rather worryingly just didn't get it at all! How many times did I have to explain that you are allowed a glass of wine with lunch in the UK? He just did not understand or accept that the assistant's attention had only been drawn to me because I had MS and poor balance. Not because I had drunk one small glass of wine! This was one of the leading supermarkets in the UK. I had no patience left and demanded to speak to someone more senior. It must be said it took the supervisor until my third attempt at explaining, for the penny to drop! Once it did, the situation gained momentum. Following our discussion, I agreed to give her the next two to three days to investigate the matter. She was astounded it had all taken place over a 187 ml bottle of wine. She was shocked that the manager had sold it to my brother. The supervisor was very apologetic about the way I had been treated and that my seven-year-old son had been witness to it.

I telephoned her back as it neared the end of the week. She apologised again and explained that a formal letter was in the post to me. She said the matter had been raised at the highest level and there had been both shock and dismay it had taken place. I felt that was as positive a response as I could have expected. The following day the post arrived. In it was my written apology, which was well received. I read with interest mostly what had been mentioned on the telephone. However, there was an additional paragraph that went on to offer me financial remuneration as way of an apology. Maybe I should have been, but I was not expecting that. The money was in return for me signing a letter stating I would not take the matter any further.

I was surprised, but in a pleasant way. I was happy to sign as it was never about gaining money, but about justice and equality. A hearty cheque followed and it was certainly time to visit the toy shop. Elliot and Helena deserved a treat to compensate for their distress in witnessing the whole sorry situation. Elliot was so happy that 'the not nice lady' had been told she was wrong and his mum had been vindicated. I must say he was not shy to tell her himself at the time in the shop. Elliot mentioned the incident on several occasions over the coming months and we talked it through many times. Just before New Year celebrations that year we were reflecting over all that had happened and without any prompting Elliot said, 'the not nice lady from the store' was the worst thing of his year. That was over six months after the event, but it was the first thought that came to his mind. Surely reason enough why people should think more of the consequences of their actions? There is no place in our society for thoughtless discrimination.

I contacted the MS Society the day after the incident. I was feeling particularly vulnerable and distressed. I spoke with someone on the telephone and they did offer support and recognise I had been through a trauma. They said they would send me through some information and MS cards that would support me in any future situations. They were small cards, the same size and style as business cards. When they arrived, I will always remember my shocked reaction. The cards did refer to the fact I had MS and may need assistance. But what sticks in my mind was the line that said on one of the cards 'I have MS, can I use your toilet?' I'm afraid I was anticipating something a bit more empowering than that. I was looking for a supporting statement, not an excuse. I do not need to apologise for having MS or feel inferior. I was an equal to everyone else in the store and do not expect to be treated the same way, I demand it. I was looking for something that would state that. I also think it is a sad and depressing case if you need to excuse yourself with a chronic disease to be able to use someone's toilet! The MS Society does work hard to reach people and meet their needs. But it was becoming clearer that they were not meeting mine.

28

The Fall

'I've learned that no matter what happens, or how bad it seems today, life does go on, and it will be better tomorrow.'
(Maya Angelou)

The fall was entirely down to me. There were no external factors. It was a Saturday afternoon in autumn 2013 and not too long after my supermarket incident. It was a cold and windy day, more suited to indoor activities. Allan and Elliot headed out for a game of tennis at the sports centre. I thought I would make good use of my time with a trip to the gym.

I planned a change to my workout. I had recently come across an article during one of my many 'Google MS' moments. It was about Montel Williams, the American presenter. He too has MS and the article was explaining that his gym input had positive effects, including walking on the treadmill.[14] I thought I would give it a try. Previously, I had avoided the treadmill through lack of confidence in my balance and coordination. I left out some of the weight machines and ten minutes on the exercise bike to compensate.

14 www.everydayhealth.com: Montel Williams's MS Routine: A juice diet and regular exercise, Mollie Bloudoff-Indelicato

I went to the gym with my sister that day. We planned our workout carefully. We decided on the smaller details, like who would hit the stop button on the treadmill if necessary! We made sure to minimise any risk. I walked on the treadmill at a very steady speed. I could feel immediately how it would help with my walking and muscle strength. All in all, I felt good and still managed a few lengths in the pool. When I got home, I was tired. That was in line though with how I would be after a session at the gym. I didn't give it any more thought.

Allan and Elliot had a great time at the tennis, though Elliot showed no signs of being tired! It was Saturday evening and we were having a DVD and buffet night! The clocks were due to go back that night so Elliot was indulging in being up a little later than usual! I was aware as the evening progressed my legs were more fatigued than they normally would be. I put it down to the fact I had started the new part of my workout. Allan took Elliot upstairs to get ready for bed and I stayed downstairs at first. Nearing the time for lights out I went up to say goodnight to Elliot, as I did every night. We had a little chat, usual bedtime cuddles and as I left his room we were still chatting. I cannot explain why, but outside his room I took a small step backwards. I do not remember what we were talking about or why I had a lapse in concentration. I wasn't attempting to move or walk. I was just standing at the top of the stairs with my back to them, finishing the conversation with Elliot. I had nothing on my feet. Plain and simple I lost my footing and my balance.

Within a split second my back hit the top stair with an angry thud. It was a very aggressive fall with my entire body hitting the ground at the same time, with no resistance. I will hauntingly never forget that moment. It is still as vivid as the day it happened, even the sound. I tried instinctively and with great panic to get hold of the wooden bars at the top of the stairs. I could feel them as my hand reached out desperately, but I could not grip onto one. My body slid backwards with speed as I went thumping down all thirteen stairs. I fell from the top to the bottom with my head thrusting backwards and forward on every step, banging against the wall as I went down. There was nothing I could do. I came to a sudden stop at the bottom. I was in complete shock and could not move or make a sound. There were no thoughts in my head. Just pain all over my body.

I could hear Elliot's screams and Allan shouting in a state of panic as they were both looking downstairs at me, lying slumped at the bottom. Allan got to me in seconds and I managed to mutter 'OK' and nothing more. All I could think about was Elliot and how I could get to him and stop this nightmare. I told Allan to leave me, more through gestures than words, as I slowly lifted my head up. I could move the top part of my body at least. Allan was stressing that I was moving at all and wanted to phone an ambulance. I needed to try to get to my feet and see Elliot. That way I could find out what the damage was. Somehow, I managed to and extremely cautiously moved with my head throbbing and stinging. Not surprisingly I was very shaky and all muscles had to be coached to make any movements. Elliot was in floods of tears as I gestured to him to come downstairs and he did with haste. I held him as best I could whilst reassuring him Mum was all right and it had been a hideous accident. I was in a lot of pain, but the greatest pain for me was seeing Elliot so upset.

Allan was extremely anxious and just kept repeating he could not believe I seemed able to move all the parts of my body. I could stand up and walk very slowly. Although there was nowhere without pain, there was nowhere without function. It felt almost impossible this had taken place. I was devastated it had happened and been witnessed by both Allan and Elliot. I felt for the first time in my life like a complete failure. It is complex to explain those feelings, but overwhelmingly I was distraught that I had let them both down. Elliot began to calm down as he was consoled that Mum was going to be all right. I moved rather shakily into the living room to sit down and consider how I was. Allan telephoned my sister to come and look after Elliot. She arrived within minutes from just around the corner. By now all I could hear from her and Allan was that I needed to go to the hospital. I was sore, very sore. There were pains shooting through my back and neck. I could feel lots of little lumps scattered across the crown of my head. My head was thumping, but I just wanted to stay in the chair. Elliot had regained his composure and we spent a few minutes together. I put on my best positive performance that I was fine and he went back upstairs with my sister.

Everything had happened within a few minutes and there had been a fair deal of noise and chaos around the house. I was, as always, reluctant to take a back seat and confident that although I was in pain, I was all right. I didn't feel I had any broken bones. Allan was insistent that because I had banged my head on all thirteen stairs, there was no possibility of that going unchecked. Unlike me, I gave in and agreed to go to the hospital. I could see the worry and strain on his face. He had suffered a huge shock and I had to try to help give him some reassurance.

We made our way to Glasgow Royal Infirmary, Accident and Emergency Department. It was around 10.00 pm on a Saturday night and that is not the place you want to be! Allan had to drop me at the front door as I was in so much pain. He caught up with me inside and we made our way very slowly to the reception area. On route, we passed cut eyes, bloody faces, and a drunken man slumped to the ground. Couples engaged in alcohol-induced warfare, and that was just the front row. I was not happy to be there. I was in pain, exhausted and angry this had happened. It was Saturday night, we'd had a good day with our sporting events, enjoyed our DVD and buffet night and were just about to switch the lights out for Elliot's bedtime. I had poured a cold glass of bubbly cava and a whisky for Allan before going up to see Elliot. All I had to do was get downstairs and Allan would have been a couple of minutes behind me.

Instead, I found myself sitting in the waiting area at Accident and Emergency surrounded by other unfortunates. I kept looking up at the clock and trying not to listen to the many conversations going on, all of which were loud and most of which were aggressive. There were police men and women all around the place, with lots of comings and goings. The time passed quickly and eventually I started to feel less agitated and more that I'd had a lucky escape. Around 11.00 pm I was called by the triage nurse who was very good and efficient. He offered me a trolley bed to lie on in the waiting room once he realised I had MS and what had happened. I swiftly declined.

Another hour passed before I was called to see a doctor. That time I did have to lie on a trolley bed and be examined from head to toe. The doctor said I would need to go for an X-ray to check my spine. She said there was nothing obvious wrong, but after such a fall it was necessary to investigate. Wheeled down the corridor by the very silent porter, I was dropped off at the 1.00 am X-ray queue. The man in the trolley next to me nodded and I politely nodded back. It's a strange place to find yourself making small talk at 1.00 am on a Sunday morning. The outcome was that I truly had a lucky escape. I was battered and bruised. I had lumps and bumps. But there were no other more sinister injuries. I could hardly keep my eyes open by that point. Allan on the other hand was more lifted. I took the painkillers they had given me, got dressed and we left the hospital.

We returned to the house around 2.30 am. My sister was waiting eagerly, but it was difficult to talk right away. I had so many emotions running through me all mixed in with exhaustion and pain. The tears just began to roll down for the first time since it had all happened and they weren't for stopping any time soon. My sister made us tea and toast, as you do at times like that! The three of us started to talk and share some of our feelings. Elliot was settled, asleep in bed. It had been a long and difficult evening and we had all suffered a big shock. It was as though the gravity of the full affair just dawned on me. Allan said very candidly, 'You dodged a bullet there Tricia.' That struck me, and the enormity of falling down thirteen steps. I felt very vulnerable at that moment.

I wanted so much to go to bed and sleep, but I was disappointingly frightened at the thought of closing my eyes. My sister left to make her way home while Allan and I spent a few moments before I had to face climbing the very stairs I had earlier fallen down. I was scared just thinking about it, but I have never been one to stop and allow fear to direct me. Instead I went straight ahead to confront it. Just before I did, I turned to Allan and asked if he was all right and what his honest thoughts were, as I was very concerned for him and what he had been through. He answered saying that I might not actually want to know. I asked him to go on and explain. He did and said that when he got to the top of the stairs and looked down with a panic-stricken Elliot by his side, he saw me crumpled in a silent, motionless heap. He said, 'I thought you were dead.'

It was with great difficulty I managed to lie down on my bed. My neck was so tender and painful. I had a silent cry as I went off to sleep, but it didn't take long as I was altogether worn out. I woke more than once with the pain and a startle each time. It was as though I was confused and big waves of panic ran through me from top to bottom. I was glad when morning arrived albeit an early morning start, as the clocks had gone back that night. Allan suggested that I stay in bed a while longer, but that was the last thing I wanted to do. I was so stiff and sore. It had been a difficult night trying to get comfortable. We still had a nice family morning and I made sure Elliot saw me managing, so that he was getting plenty of reassurance. I took some more painkillers and was feeling very stiff, with my movement restricted.

It was a big day in Allan's football calendar with Partick Thistle playing Celtic. Allan had a season ticket for Thistle and I insisted he went. He was feeling unsure about leaving me, but I couldn't think of anywhere better for him to release any pent-up tension and forget his troubles for a short while. He agreed to go. I was not going to be on my own. My day was to consist of sitting on my comfy chair with hot water bottles, painkillers and my beloved iPad! My brother and sister came around and made lunch. We watched the football match on television. Allan made his way to Firhill Stadium for what was to be another defeat!

I had many flashbacks and it was a long day. Elliot wanted to stay in his pyjamas and he was very clingy. We laughed, played and told stories. Elliot was continuously being reassured that Mum was all right. I wanted to wipe it all away for him. Being with him, giving him lots of positive messages and visuals was as close as I was going to get. Kids can be very resilient and Elliot was surely displaying that. I did everything to make things as normal as possible. Although he was playing games and distracted we still talked a lot and I made sure he didn't feel the need to bottle up his thoughts or worries.

On the Monday morning, I woke to excruciating pain, mostly in my neck. I decided to go and see my own GP. Dr Lyndsay listened as always with empathy and attention to every detail. She said too that I had a lucky escape and the neck pain was whiplash, which would relieve only with time. I had the painkillers from the hospital in the meantime when I needed them. Although they exacerbated my fatigue, I still had to take them to get some pain relief. That Monday was the worst day. I was in constant pain and not in a good frame of mind. Elliot was at school so I could drop the 'I'm OK' front and be a bit more honest with myself. It was mostly a day of painkillers and sitting. With that came a lot of thinking time and my mood was lower than it had been in a long, long while. But as always in my life, Elliot arrived home from school and the low mood had to go hide somewhere else. It was homework and healthy snack time and nothing stood in the way of that. I was able to lift myself, as I always could, when he was around. Elliot made no reference to the fall at all that Monday.

The next day I was feeling a bit better and my mood was a little closer to where it should be. I still had pain and limited movement, but it was less than the previous day. As each day passed my recovery progressed well and within a few days I could do some of my daily activities without too much pain and restriction. I began to feel very much more positive again and after only five days I was back in the swimming pool. Even I didn't envisage that, but I never cease to surprise myself! It was an attempt to stretch my neck and back. A very distressing event had been turned around in only days and I felt I was on my way back to my near normal state. At that point I was feeling pleased with my recovery and was back on my determined path.

It had been an upsetting experience, but the important

thing was to try not to let it cause any more upset. Elliot did not mention it for a few days and seemed to be coping remarkably well. He was back to school, football, Halloween parties and non-stop ideas! He was moving on and so should I, but I would always be ready to talk when he wanted to. For the time being though it was game on and time to get back on that treadmill of life again. Maybe not literally! I just hoped the strong confident surge would last and was not just a temporary bounce-back reaction. Time would tell.

29

Getting Back Up

*'The greatest glory in living lies not in never falling, but in
rising every time we fall.'*

(Nelson Mandela)

I was wrong. It didn't last very long. It seemed so
straightforward in the aftermath of the fall. I had got up
a bit battered and bruised and charged straight on with
life again. I was back into my daily routine and things
were as 'normal' as they got in my life. But the weeks that
followed were to take me a little by surprise. I managed
that one slow swim, but the injuries from the fall meant I
couldn't do much more and my body was telling me not
to. That wasn't good for me, either physically or mentally.
Going to the gym was important to my strength and
mobility. I was concerned.

I started the next week with a bad cold and that added
to the fact I could do even less. The week after that Elliot
became unwell and was off school with the reappearance
of eczema he had as a baby. That was possibly a sudden
flare-up caused by stress. I spent the week looking after
him and it was my third consecutive week indoors.
During that time, I did very little as my damaged body

needed to rest. Since the fall and for the first time ever, I felt physically unable to manage things. My mood was going down all the time. I wasn't willing and I wasn't able. Living in a house with stairs left no option but to be up and down them throughout the day. That was a big and uncomfortable problem for me. My confidence had taken a real knock and I was having recurring flashbacks. That just kept happening to me over the days and weeks that followed the fall. I tried to battle with the flashbacks and the overwhelming fear I would fall again. The dread was that next time the outcome would be more sinister. I wasn't winning that battle.

My fear was not to lessen for some time and even then, it was not to go away for good. That fall, without serious damage, was not to end there. It continued to cause a great deal of grief and distress over a long period. I began concentrating even more than before on each step I took. That itself was exhausting. I am unsure if that will ever leave me or if in fact it ever can. I must ensure, to the best of my ability, a similar fall does not happen again. There is a line however, where that crosses into hypervigilance and has a significantly negative impact. I am still striving to get the right balance, but it is a tough call. I have walked and observed my surroundings intensely ever since the fall. I do not like the feelings of being tense or the fear it has engendered in me, but unfortunately there is little I can do to change that. Whilst I am on the move, out and about, up and down stairs, that is just the way it has to be. Time has not eased that.

The weeks passed and things remained difficult. With Christmas (2013) fast approaching my mood was still worryingly low. It was going to be difficult to lift myself. I hadn't felt like that since my diagnosis. I was a strong person and it took a lot to knock me off my stride. I was always positive and ready to overcome any obstacles put in my way. Unfortunately, I was tired of battling every single day and those past weeks had just been too much. I felt I was losing the very long battle with Multiple Sclerosis for the first time. I had an overwhelming feeling I was just going through the motions. I wasn't cooking my usual healthy foods and so wasn't eating as I should have been. I was out so little it could not be good for my mental and emotional health. I stopped communicating with anyone outside of my few close family members. It was very cold by that point which only added to the fact I went out less. I made the odd trip to the local supermarket or a visit to my mum's house. I collected Elliot from school too, but that was about all I felt up to or interested in.

Christmas shopping just wasn't an option, although if I'm honest I was happy to shop online. I usually did in any case. It was simply a matter of sitting down with the iPad and using my shortcut to the Amazon UK webpage. Together we were sorted in no time. Well, more or less! Click and collect filled in the gaps. Sooner than expected I had managed to wrap up most of Christmas. An online grocery shop would finish it off. All of that had been done from the comfort of my sofa and so I learned that although I was down, I was not in fact out. I had focussed on organising the physical tasks of Christmas, but I still had to address my emotional state. That left the battle between motherhood and Multiple Sclerosis at a challenging place. Christmas was nearly upon us and Elliot was excited. I had to put my feelings aside somehow and lift myself for the coming festivities. I had been battling MS for over seven years and for the first time, I felt it had become a bit bigger than me. I was tired, I was at home far too much and I was not attending the gym. I was still sore physically and emotionally from that drastic fall.

Deep down I knew some fun family time over the festive period would do me a lot of good. We always loved the holidays from school and the daily routine. I knew I had to lift the weighty cloud I was living under so that Elliot, along with the rest of the family, would have a good Christmas. It was not a matter of if I should do it, but more accurately how. Every time Elliot's eyes lit up with excitement it helped me edge a little further forward. What I needed was deep courage and I was certainly lacking in that department. My confidence was not returning like it had in the immediate aftermath. I had to work harder than expected. On reflection, I felt life was getting a bit too tough. That was not a luxury I often afforded myself. It was not a place I was comfortable in, but reluctantly found myself there.

It was nearly time for the school Christmas disco and being a member of the Parent Council, I always helped at such events. On that occasion, nothing could have been further from my mind. But oh no, Elliot was to announce he only wanted to go if I was going to be there! He was familiar with Mum helping at school and very comfortable with that in the infant years. A tiny bit of the real me stepped forward. If it meant that much to Elliot, I would do it. No thoughts, no qualms. A disco ticket was bought for Elliot and I was doing the tuck shop with the other mums. That small request of Elliot's opened my mind up and made me take the first step, since my fall, of going out and doing something I didn't need to do.

I arrived at the school hall on a freezing December night for the Christmas disco. It was the first time I had put myself out there since the fall and the real dent in my self-belief. I was questioning my whole self-help journey and the choices I had made. No one else there knew anything about how I was feeling. I just presented as my usual self. I found the tuck shop had been set out on the stage. Only two small steps up to reach it, but with nothing to hold on to. To me it could just as well have been a mountain! *Oh dear!* I thought as I walked over, trying to think on the spot how I would overcome this one. Luckily no one else was there yet so I managed to get up, albeit rather clumsily, with the help of Elliot's hand and the table. Once up on the stage that was me 'marooned' until further notice!

The evening passed and although I felt uncomfortable the whole time because my feet were not firmly on the ground, I managed well. Interacting with the children lifted my spirits. All I had to plan was my ungainly descent when it was time to go home! I had arranged for my sister to come inside the hall to meet me and she did. She knew instinctively the issue. She waltzed on stage and whispered curiously, asking how I had got up there. I said that it had not been done gracefully, but had been achieved despite the challenge. No one had been around to witness it and therefore luckily no one would ever know!

At the close of the disco we wrapped things up and my sister helped with the necessary manoeuvres to exit from the back of the stage. Again, it was rather uncoordinated, but with her support I managed and chose not to turn around to see if anyone was looking. It was such a simple thing to move the tuck shop onto the stage, but one that put up real barriers and created obstacles for me! The good news was I could overcome them and with confidence again. That simple request from Elliot to be a parent helper at the school disco became so much more than just that. It started my return to the former spirit I had always used to confront MS. It was indeed the answer to my question as to how I was going to lift the cloud I was living under. If I'm completely honest I even found small amusement in the whole thing! I was at last on the road to feeling like myself again. I had a long way to go, but I had felt that first spark. It meant a lot.

Once the festive period had passed, we could get back on with family life. I was on that road to recovery, but I undoubtedly had to clear away the hefty feeling of hardship and fear around me. It was going to be difficult to shift my feelings back to positive ones as it felt that every time I managed to sort one thing, something else would go wrong. I was to brace myself for another year ahead and all that it may bring. I still believed in me and that I would rise to the challenges that lay ahead. I didn't believe, however, there would be as many good times and good things ahead. The adversity seemed to outweigh the positives in my life and that was a new chapter. It was the most difficult time in my MS journey. Deep, deep down I still had hope that the tide would turn and faith in those around me.

That all happened around the time Nelson Mandela passed away and I was continually hearing positive, courageous statements from throughout his life:

'After climbing a great hill one only finds that there are many more hills to climb.'

That quote stuck with me and felt most pertinent in my life. It was perfectly acceptable to have had a significant dip, as I had been faced with some real challenges. What was not acceptable however was to give in. I wasn't familiar or comfortable with feeling negative and defeatist. I was not best pleased with myself that I had succumbed to MS and all that falls out from having it. But I was big enough to admit I had. My human spirit that up until then knew no bounds had been broken a little. But it was repairable. I had been through a traumatic part of my journey and it was time to make my way back to where I was before the fall. I realised though that things would not stay the same and I accepted that. I was under an umbrella of cautiousness from then on. I still am and that fall has left a mark I cannot ever see leaving me. It happened so simply that I feel there is no option but to concentrate and focus at every waking moment. That is an enormous pressure to live with. I started very slowly, but nonetheless I started, to build my confidence and regain some of my physical strength. I set myself small, achievable goals and worked hard to reach them. The more I did, the better I felt and began to turn things around little by little. Life goes on no matter what and I had managed to find some strength again. Thanks to Elliot for inspiring me and Mandela for redirecting me. It had been the toughest of times, but I could see a little light at the end of the darkest tunnel.

30

Another Setback

'Man never made any material as resilient as the human spirit.'

(Bernard Williams)

Only weeks later, at the beginning of the New Year (2014), I got some disheartening news. I received a letter to say Dr Gilhooly would no longer be holding private clinics. That came as a real shock and hit me hard. It most definitely did not help my ongoing recovery. The timing was unkind to say the least. I lived with an inner confidence because I had Dr Gilhooly as my consultant and that meant I was not alone when it came to medical guidance.

Life with Multiple Sclerosis produces countless experiences, which come out of the blue. That one hit me harder than others. I searched to find out what had happened. I was trying to get some understanding of why there had been such a dramatic change of direction from Dr Gilhooly. Suffice to say that there had been an intervention by the GMC (General Medical Council), here in the UK, in relation to prescribing LDN. Regardless of the circumstances, Dr Gilhooly was an amazing doctor, who looked after the interests of his patients and strived for a better quality of life for them. To put it bluntly, life without Dr Gilhooly on your side just got a whole lot harder for a lot of people. There would seem no reason not to prescribe LDN to someone like myself. I only take a small dosage daily of 2.5 mls. This drug was once deemed safe to prescribe in doses of 50 mls and above for other medical use. The relentless campaign is far and wide in different countries around the world trying to have it licensed to prescribe in lower doses. It is cheap and many people who take it have shown positive results. I am one of those people and was put in a situation where I had to find another doctor to prescribe it. That caused a great deal of uncertainty initially and even when it was resolved, I had still lost Dr Gilhooly as my consultant, putting me back in the same position as I was post-diagnosis. I think it is to the eternal shame of the medical profession that they appear to operate the protocol of: if it doesn't fit the mould then it isn't getting licensed. That seems to stand whether the treatment is suggested to benefit patients or not. I have had absolutely no side effects from LDN. I cannot say the same thing about countless prescription drugs.

I was alone once again with regards to vital medical support or intervention. I often have burning questions about my MS and the things I am doing to manage it. I have returned to the position of having no one to talk to about it. That is both unnerving and unsettling. The painful pressure has reappeared to keep myself moving forward with the management of my MS. That is not a comfortable position to find myself in.

That was only compounded shortly afterwards with the news that Dr Leckridge, the homeopathic doctor from the Centre for Integrative Care, was retiring in the summer of that same year. Again, it gave me great security to be able to talk to him freely and always find out new information and answers to my questions, of which there were many. Dr Leckridge provided holistic care and always allowed unrestricted opportunity to talk about personal and emotional circumstances. That was invaluable to my overall well-being. At my final consultation with him, only weeks before his retirement, we discussed the many things I had been doing to aid my well-being physically, emotionally and financially. Dr Leckridge's final message will always stay with me. He said 'Keep doing what you're doing, you are doing all the right things.'

It was certainly a bleak time in my journey and one where I had to stop and think. I was deeply determined, however, not to be plunged back into the darkness of the previous months. I had to look forward and see which direction I should go in, but that would take some time. I was at least more equipped with wider knowledge and personal experience about MS than I had been in those initial stages. It seemed likely I would stay on the same path, but with awareness I may need some support in the future. I would be on high alert for someone else, but I wasn't sure if you could ever replace the likes of Dr Gilhooly or Dr Leckridge. It had been a privilege to be one of their patients.

Life still had to go on and so, without delay, I sourced a new prescriber for my LDN. The dispensing pharmacy facilitated that. I had a very brief telephone consultation with a doctor from the new clinic consisting of two closed questions and a prescription subsequently authorised. There was a 400% increase in administration costs from Dr Gilhooly's clinic. A bitter pill to swallow. I had my medication, but no more medical care attached. The General Medical Council may not have thought through the wider consequences of their actions. For me though it was time to keep going forward, despite my disappointment and the setback it brought. There was nothing else for it. Like everything else surrounding Multiple Sclerosis, nothing stays the same.

It was not long until I discovered that the Baseline AM and PM supplements, by Dr Gilhooly, were no longer available. I searched and searched, but to no avail. I had to go back to the drawing board to look at my supplement intake and balance. It was an enforced overhaul and I stretched it to include my overall dietary and nutritional consumption. It took some time to get a good balance again. Once more I had to dig deep and adapt.

All the changes did not help my mission trying to climb back up from that horrible fall and all it had brought with it. The burden felt undeservingly heavier, but I made a commitment to myself that it was time to start a new chapter in my MS journey.

31

Hope Returns

'Hope is tomorrow's veneer over today's disappointment.'

(Evan Esar)

Everything that had happened could not be changed, so it seemed appropriate to leave it behind. I had to shake off those feelings of doom and gloom and start looking ahead with hope and aspiration. The winter had not helped with the many difficulties encountered. It was extremely cold, which meant many long days indoors. The dark nights signified even less activity and I never did cope particularly well with the lack of sunlight hours in winter time. I had lost Dr Gilhooly in my journey. In short, the hill in front of me to climb had just got a lot bigger.

As 2014 got underway, I decided enough was enough. I launched myself into a healthy diet and increased my intake of raw vegetable juices. I ate five to ten portions of fresh fruit and vegetables a day. I took my protein smoothie daily as well as protein bars from the health shop. Alongside that I drank copious amounts of water and herbal tea, mainly green tea. I came across kamboucha tea and pure ginger drinks, adding those into my diet. It was absolutely time to get back in the swimming pool, whether it was freezing outside or not! It was the start I needed to turn around the fortunes of the previous months.

I needed to build on that start. What had become over many years my MS jigsaw had remained just a little bit too static for some time as life had got in the way. It was the last thing I wanted. But with Allan running his own small business from home, the demands of childcare along with domestic jobs, it had become harder and harder to prioritise my well-being and needs. In some weird and inexplicable way, that fall took me to a place where I had no alternative. I had to pay attention to my MS jigsaw again and dig deep in search of positives, but I would not rest until I uncovered some. I required help and I needed hope. Diet and exercise were the backbone of my self-help approach, but there was something missing. Before Dr Gilhooly had stopped his private practice, he had introduced me to something called earthing.

Earthing (sometimes called grounding) is suggested to be 'The most important health discovery ever?'[15] It quite simply means connecting to the earth's natural surface. That should be done barefoot outside or with bare skin contact to a conductive system whilst you are doing something indoors. I had tried earthing in my back garden, but the unpredictable and cold Scottish weather prevented me from doing it on a regular basis. I did wrap up and sit with green tea and hot water bottles, but

---

15 *Earthing: The most important health discovery ever?* Clinton Ober, Dr Stephen T. Sinatra M.D., Martin Zucker, Basic Health Publications Inc, 25.04.2010

eventually the plummeting temperatures put a stop to it! That all changed when I was given an earthing mat for my birthday. I was at home more due to that fall and started earthing on a regular basis indoors.

It is a very straightforward concept and one that is open to everyone. When you are in direct contact with the earth it is suggested that 'you're receiving a surge of potent healing electrons from the ground.'[16] Those electrons are scientifically believed to have a positive impact on inflammation in the body. We are all aware of the benefits of the sun and trying to catch some rays whenever it makes an appearance. Earthing focusses on the goodness we can get by connecting to the ground. It was something that was a normal part of life for hundreds of years. I had earthed, indoors mostly, since I got my earthing mat. I enjoyed it, felt good and looked out for its benefits.

Ongoing at the time was my New Year plan. I was committed to keeping as active as possible. I had agreed with myself I would make the odd bus journey again to school in the new term. I wanted to push myself that little bit further and challenge my ever-changing abilities. I reluctantly, but with determination, travelled by bus. I awkwardly walked down the hill into the school yard and on arrival, unexpectedly felt good. I noticed a marked change in how things had been over the last couple of months and since my fall. I had not needed to dig as deep to make the journey. That was pleasantly unusual. My legs had more power and were moving better than they

16 www.mercola.com: Grounding Is a Key Mechanism by Which
Your Body Maintains Health, Dr Mercola, 02.08.2014

normally did. I decided to test this further by walking back up the hill with Elliot. As I progressed towards the top my legs felt somewhat lighter. At the top where the ever-smiling lollipop lady, Mrs Doyle, stood, I was not my usual weary self. That was an extremely uplifting moment, even though it relates to something as basic as walking up the hill to the bus stop after school with your son. That would be a moment to write that I had a skip in my step but, as that evades me, the elation remained internal! Those kerbs in front of me to cross did not seem the giants they used to be! As I waited at the bus stop and Elliot ran around with the other children, my legs felt like they still had something left in them. That was not something you would normally associate with me by that point. On our arrival home I did not feel the immediate need to sit and recover. I was unsure what to put the positive progress down to.

I found it difficult to enjoy the moment for fear of when the feeling might leave me. One of the hardest facts to come to terms with is that circumstances change all the time. A positive change may not be sustained past a few hours. Something I could manage comfortably one day is out of my reach only the next. There is nothing I can do about any of those things and that is very challenging, both physically and emotionally, to reconcile. I tried to ascertain what had led to that uplifting experience. My MS jigsaw had a new piece in it: earthing. So, was it that or simply my improved diet and exercise routine?

Like many things I will be unable to ever say conclusively what made the real difference to my walking and mobility on that day. What I do know is I had not been as able for a long time. On the following day, I set off again to collect Elliot from school. I was a bit nervous as we embarked on our journey home. Yes, it was better than it had been. No, it was not as good as the day before. I had mixed emotions as we reached the lollipop lady that time. The overriding feeling was to stay with the fact that my walking was still a little better than it had been in recent weeks. I try not to let any positives pass me by.

That tiny, teensy, bit of hope I carried that possibly my walking had improved for the longer term was gone. I have had so much experience of a symptom or flare-up improving somewhat, only for it to come back. But I was still left with the fact there had been an improvement and so that gave me hope. It was not easy accepting it was no longer the same. However, I try to be big enough as a person to remember that it did happen and so it can happen again. My spirit had been lifted, albeit temporarily. Like all things with MS it's difficult to get consistency and stability, but if I can get positive change at times, improvement at times, good days mixed in with the more challenging ones then I will stick with every different thing I have tried.

I have continued with the earthing as well as my dietary effort and exercise. There is always hope that something around the corner will improve my quality of life. The weeks that followed brought with them days where my legs felt stronger and my balance better. Then there were days where my legs went back to feeling heavy and cumbersome and my balance was not at its best, to say the least. Which day would bring what, I would have little idea of. My dad always said, 'Go with the flow' and there would be no better descriptor of how I should live my life. My mood was most certainly lifted. There were both significant physical and emotional improvements. I was back putting that jigsaw together again. The year 2014 marked a new chapter in my MS journey, brought about by the loss of Dr Gilhooly and that devastating fall. I used those experiences as an opportunity to bring more support into my MS life and build not only my confidence, but practical, doable steps to raise the bar on my ability. Earthing was a good starting point along with my exceptional dietary improvements and exercise. Hope had returned.

32

Earthing

'I think being different, going against the grain of society is the greatest thing in the world.'

(Elijah Wood)

With the belief that earthing was making a difference, no matter how small, I decided I would put it to the test when summer arrived that year and some better weather with it. My research had brought me the enlightening news that the best benefits of earthing may be experienced with your feet in water. Unusually it was a reasonably warm summer here in Scotland with a fair bit of sunshine. I embarked on my mission starting with a day trip to the beach at Seamill on the Ayrshire coast, here in Scotland. It was about an hour's drive from my house. It is probably my favourite place in the world. I have always found visits to Seamill uplifting and inspiring, so there seemed no better location to head to. It is a very rugged and rocky beach area, often accompanied by high winds and cool temperatures no matter the season! Very Scottish indeed! My sister drove there and we made our way to the water's edge with our plastic storage boxes to sit on! We dipped our feet in the sea and had to push ourselves back every few minutes as the tide came in! It was a very enjoyable and thoroughly refreshing activity! There were a few strange and shifty looks at these two forty-somethings sitting on plastic boxes with their feet in the sea! Only once we were too cold did we pack up and head back to the car. We drove home and I felt a little tired, similar to after having a therapeutic massage or treatment.

Once home I began to feel more energised and stayed up that little bit later than usual to watch the quarter-final of the football World Cup which was on at the time. That was novel for me. My feet still felt 'lively' as the evening progressed. I retired to bed that night with a tiny thought sitting somewhere in my head that maybe I was onto something with this idea of earthing by the water. The next morning, I put my feet onto the floor to get out of bed only to discover there were strong tingling sensations in my left toes. I could feel parts of them for the first time in many years. It felt amazing and even more so that it could have come from earthing with my feet on the sand in the seawater. I only told Allan as with most changes, positive or negative with me and Multiple Sclerosis, they are not permanent. My instinct was right once again and by the end of the day numbness and that uncomfortable tight feeling had returned. I had enjoyed the whole experience and did not feel too down-hearted. It was hard to come to terms with the reality that it was so short-lived, but that was just the way. Instead, I considered carefully what my next step would be to pursue this activity further.

I had arranged a couple of trips up to the north of Scotland during the school holidays. On both trips, I made a point to earth each day. That time it was at the most beautiful lochs in Scotland. I would sit on the lochside with my feet in the fresh water and found one that hosted a sandy beach. I always felt stimulated, relaxed and spritely. I was overlooking the snow-capped Cairngorm Mountains as I was doing it. What is of greater interest is that throughout each day I had more energy and lots of tingling sensations centred on my feet. I always felt immediate calmness as my feet entered the water. I could do more than I was generally able to manage and very importantly I felt good within myself. I began to think I had found an amazing piece of the jigsaw. One that was very effective – and into the bargain free for a change!

I returned home from my holidays thinking of ways to continue earthing. I did have a garden, but had felt more benefit at the seaside and lochside. It was certainly going to be a challenge, but with my usual attitude, eagerness and support we would 'findaway'! We travelled as and when we could to the seaside for the rest of the summer and beyond. I always felt at my best after earthing in seawater. My constant fact-finding investigations revealed that salt water is a great conductor of the free electrons from the earth to your body.[17] We went to Seamill almost every time and on one of those occasions we tried to use folding chairs instead of plastic boxes. Not one of my better ideas, as the chair keeled over into the sea with me still on it! As it sank into the wet sand, in almost slow motion, there was nothing I could do to stop it! My balance was completely out of sorts on the soft, malleable

17 www.earthinginstitute.net: Earthing Basics, FAQs, Are you grounded in water – the ocean, a lake, your swimming pool, your bathtub?

sand. I laughed and laughed and was hugely embarrassed as the local dog-walkers ran to rescue me! Very wet and muddy, but exhilarated nonetheless, we left the beach that day!

Otherwise I earthed in my own garden. I even brought seawater back home to pour onto my grass. Everything's worth a try and there is nothing I won't give a try! Elliot would just look out in the garden and say, 'Mum's earthing again!' I loved the fact it was so normal to him. He is very broad and open-minded for a child of his age. I felt huge rewards from earthing and had a big headache ahead of me thinking of ways I could continue it throughout the winter months. I had the indoor earthing mat, but had felt a noticeable difference doing it in the natural elements of the great outdoors, with the key to it being by the waterside.

When I was back in the swing of my regular routine, the positive benefits of earthing began to subside. They did not leave me in their entirety straightaway, but the impact was significantly lessened. General fatigue accompanied by dizziness did reappear once I was back doing household jobs along with cooking. I had thoroughly enjoyed some respite from such symptoms. I would have to continue in the knowledge I had the ability to alleviate them from time to time, but that it was not sustainable in amongst the rest of life. Even though that was difficult news to accept, it meant I had a great big bag of hope with me. It would be dishonest not to mention that the changes not being sustainable led to a great deal of frustration. But I had the priceless hope and knowledge I had another weapon in this battle against MS, which could support me in future times.

Earthing had made a super contribution to my self-help journey and so I carried on with renewed ambition. What is abundantly clear is that I must live life to the best of my ability and grab every opportunity when I am feeling able and well. We can all feel different in life from day to day. Everyone gets run-down and performs under par from time to time. Multiple Sclerosis exaggerates that and we need to allow ample rest to recover. But it is essential, for me, to keep it in perspective and not let it overwhelm me. If I'm having a good MS day, then I always turn that into a great day. If I'm having a bad MS day, then I'll slow down, rest or stop. I always embrace opportunities when I am able and equally I embrace opportunities when I am not as able. They are very different times, but I still try to find a positive in everything. Playing cards, resting with Elliot is super. Watching a film on the sofa together with a 'goody' plate is top fun! It is a matter of accepting and adapting.

I had acquired a new, positive and free tool to use as and when I could in my lifelong battle with Multiple Sclerosis. It was not something I could do and get the benefit of every day and consistently, but it was most definitely a pivotal piece of my MS jigsaw. Life was unquestionably on the up.

33

Counselling

'Above all, be the heroine of your life, not the victim.'
(Nora Ephron)

There was more hope and positivity coming my way through the unexpected route of counselling. It was something I had discussed with my GP, but I'd had MS for almost eight years when I agreed to attend. It had been put to me that it may be a welcome and supportive move to talk to someone outside of friends and family.

I met with the counsellor, Alan McNeill. I was unsure initially when I found out it was a male therapist, as I was a little more anxious about whether I would be able to relate to him on an emotional level. There was no need as I warmed to him immediately, not to mention the fact I should not have been making such a judgement! He had skills I didn't even know existed! The way I would describe it is that he opened me up like a book. I was comfortable to talk and even more comfortable to listen. I was able through the counselling to be honest with myself first and foremost. The feelings of failure were immense. Possibly not rational, but still real. The therapist raised my awareness of how I could open up and let my husband,

Allan, in more to my thoughts and feelings. I had been hiding from the truth. I had been unable to share my innermost feelings, even with myself, until then. The fact I am writing this demonstrates that the counselling was so constructive and successful. The counsellor took me on a journey I never expected to go on. I was already a very reflective person and evaluated myself and my life on a continual basis. I didn't think there were many places I still had to go internally. I was very wrong.

Counselling allowed me to start the process of accepting myself with Multiple Sclerosis. Until then, I had been feisty and spirited about the whole matter. Those were essential qualities in relation to managing MS, but I yearned for some internal peace. That was not going to be an easy task, but it was important to my progression as a person with a chronic condition. It is complex to explain, but involved shifting my perspective on most things in my life so that I could become more comfortable with my 'different' abilities. It didn't happen overnight, but there has been a sizeable and positive switch in my attitude and thoughts over months and years. It has been a slow and long process, but a very liberating one.

I had started writing my book just before attending counselling and when the two came together they had a powerful and positive impact. As I wrote down my story it opened up a lot of feelings. The truly inspiring counselling sessions helped me to make sense of them. Writing and talking about my thoughts gave me the chance to reflect on all I had achieved and coped with since my diagnosis. It made me look at my family life and how despite MS, it is a great family life and there is a whole lot of enjoyment and success there. I hadn't given myself or my family enough credit for how we had coped. MS had shifted the goal posts, but we had adapted to that shift. We had managed somehow to stay focussed and all in all achieved a very normal, rounded family life. The counsellor made it possible for me to see all of that. Thus, I am more content with myself. I even managed to forgive myself for my 'failings'. Allan and I became closer, if that were possible. I let him in to my deepest and darkest feelings. Once the counsellor pointed out how hurtful and difficult it must have been for him, I did it without hesitation. It was also easy to do because I would never knowingly hurt Allan and I love him unconditionally. I just had to talk to myself first and recognise my fears and feelings, before I could talk to anyone else. I did say the counsellor was good.

He introduced me to the concept of 'mindfulness'. 'It has its origins in ancient meditation practices.'[18] Suffice to say that it is a practice which asks you to focus your awareness on the present moment. Not to go over what has happened in the past or what indeed you may think or worry will happen in the future. It asks that you do all of that in a non-judgemental manner. That is quite challenging for anyone, not least of all me. I am very much a thinker and a planner. My mind usually races at great speed. With all the planning and looking ahead I need to do, as well as concentrating on my surroundings, it is not an easy task. I am working hard to integrate mindfulness into my life.

---

18 www.mindfulnet.org: What is Mindfulness?

From the onset, it improved my sleep pattern and helped me slow down a little. The counsellor suggested I enrol in an eight-week course. I was more than happy to do so. However, I was not able to complete the course. The classes were held in a renovated house at the top of a very steep hill. On the days Allan could not drive me it was stressful and difficult getting there and back. Sitting on a chair for two hours at each class caused my legs to stiffen up and movement at the end of the class was troublesome. There were no break times during the sessions, which I needed to move around and prevent my body becoming stiff. I disappointingly reacted after the class with a long stretch of fatigue and a severe headache. Halfway through the course, I felt I had learned enough to bring mindfulness into my life. It didn't feel necessary to continue trying to overcome all the obstacles that attending presented to me, therefore I stopped. I continue to practise and find the positive benefits to be unrivalled. Yet another piece to add to my MS jigsaw.

Counselling helped me over the one big hurdle that lived with me day in and day out. People knowing I have Multiple Sclerosis. When I told people following my diagnosis all those years back they immediately jumped to judging me and interfering with thoughts and opinions on what I should and shouldn't do. I struggled immensely with that and always will. Publishing my book will make it public and I learned that is what I need to do. Counselling allowed me to come to terms with that transition. I can even accept the voices uttering they knew there was something 'wrong' with me all along! I see more of my achievements and how valuable my resilience has been. I do feel that I have coped remarkably, if it is acceptable to say so. My wish now would be that others see all I can do and have done. That, in some way, has been the point of all this. If I had given myself a 'label' in the first instance, I would have become the person who can't do things because of her condition. By now I hope I have shown that is not the case. It was for those reasons I chose not to tell people I had MS. I couldn't have said any of this before I attended counselling. I did not think I needed it and was originally persuaded to go for a referral. It was an exceptional decision and thank you to my husband Allan for prompting it.

Counselling renewed my outlook to focus entirely on what I can do and achieve, despite Multiple Sclerosis. In fact, I would go as far as to say it reinvigorated my spirit and commitment to do so. My confidence from earlier years has re-emerged. I do not see the large clouds hanging over me anymore that held me back for some time. In fairness to myself who had all those thoughts to consider and contend with, this whole thing has been a process and a journey. I have learned something at every juncture. I learned a lot from counselling.

My MS jigsaw was surely getting bigger, bringing with it greater hope and improved health. I was grateful for all the experiences and their contribution. I was coming to terms with things I did not even know I had a problem with. Elliot was growing up and I was shedding a lot of the pain and anxiety that had been with me ever since Elliot and Multiple Sclerosis had been 'born together'.

34

Writing

'There is nothing to writing. All you do is sit down at a typewriter and bleed.'

(Ernest Hemingway)

My progress and improvement continued through writing. After the many, many years I had considered writing a book, the time was right. I started to write down my story and share my journey. Writing became a major player – and very quickly. It came from nowhere and was rapidly vying for pole position. I relished it from the very first day. I cannot give a reason why I chose the day I did to start writing down my story. The idea had lived with me for a long time, but in the end, it was a very impulsive decision. One morning after Elliot had gone to school I just picked up the iPad and never looked back. Writing opened up my feelings which had been under lock and key for too many years. At the same time, it served for me to confront those emotions and pave the way to begin coming to terms with them. I hoped it would help liberate me a little and I would find some inner peace.

From the first few days of putting my ideas down it grew arms and legs. At first it would be every two to three days, depending on how busy I was. As the weather grew colder and more unpredictable throughout that winter, it became easier to stay in and write. As time went on I realised the enormity of what I was attempting to do. The first few months were a gentle introduction to it, but the writing soon became a sizeable piece. I wrote for a couple of hours at a time to begin with. I kept that up for a few months, but it wasn't going fast enough for me! Much of the blame for that pointed towards my MS. I had to choose on which day I would do what. I couldn't write on the same day as doing any domestic chores. My body wouldn't allow me to. If I wrote for any considerable time, when I stood up I would be off balance and disorientated for a while. Therefore, I could not write on the same day I was collecting Elliot from school. If I did I had to take a taxi to the school. Once I was editing and Allan was working away a lot, it was a taxi up and down to school every day. It had to be done if I wanted to get on and finish the book. There were so many rules and considerations to work around. It was itself tiring and without a shadow of a doubt exasperating. I could only do the minimum number of domestic tasks, as it was too disruptive otherwise. I had come across a random author's story online, which said that anyone wishing to be an author could not possibly have a clean house. Plain and simple that was me off the hook! The piles of papers and books littered around the house did spiral out of control. They were in constant competition for space with Elliot's toys. Let's just say that the concept of a 'lived-in' house was taken to extremes!

That hideous fall happened in the throes of my writing. It eventually became the reason I would sit for hours on end, typing away on the iPad, allowing my writing to grow to a considerable length. There is always a positive. Before long it was time to graduate from the iPad and start using the laptop, with dedicated writing times and days planned in. It was all I wanted to do. I fitted in doing other necessities around my writing. I found that for the first time since my early teaching days I was doing something I enjoyed. Obviously becoming a mum was wonderful and since then I hadn't considered doing anything that involved just me. Writing had been merely an idea before. It seemed an overwhelming task to contemplate. That was not least because I had MS and the additional complications it would bring. Despite all of that I set about doing it on what became my 'writing chair'. My diet consisted of copious amounts of green tea and Belvita breakfast biscuits! I did stop and have days where I would do some cooking. Not that many though, as writing was much more fun! After many months of writing and editing, it was equivalent to a full-time job with overtime thrown in!

Nothing comes without sacrifice. If I had stayed with my strict programme of exercise and finely tuned diet, there would be no book. I have said before that I've always been someone who slipped 'off the wagon' and then got up and on it again. It was just another one of those slippage times, but did last longer than anticipated. I didn't see anyone socially. Even spending time with family became a rarity. I did have to re-engage with exercise after a year of writing obsessively as I was noticing deterioration with my mobility. Everything I do has a price to pay, but there's nothing I want to do that I won't consider paying that price for. Writing my book was as high up the list as you could get.

I would sit with the laptop whilst Elliot played his games on the iPad next to me. That was always nice and just another way of spending time together. He would read and ask me questions about what I was writing. I even became familiar with sitting writing in one corner of the room whilst Elliot leapt about wrestling and playing one of his many role-play games! I could just go into my little bit of head-space and it often inspired me. So, it was never about having clearly defined writing opportunities in the end. It was the usual wecanfindaway.com approach and working around the restrictions having MS placed upon me, as well as being a mum with all the daily tasks and asks! My book was written piecemeal over a few years. Elliot was always the priority. I had to stop and start continuously. Hence editing and revising took so long as I would duplicate, forget and lose my train of thought often. Once again Allan was fully supportive. He saved it every night on 'sticks' and 'clouds'. We worked as a team as always. It was just something I loved doing.

All those years after my diagnosis and I had real purpose and direction again, outside that of motherhood. Since the onset of MS there had been nothing other than Elliot that I focussed on. Elliot, along with my self-help journey, left me with little time for anything else. Writing gave me structured days once more. I had always seemed to keep busy, but that was a different kind of busy. I found the whole process very therapeutic and it helped me progress as a person. Up until I started writing I had internalised almost all my thoughts and emotions about having Multiple Sclerosis. They had been bottled up for a long time and it was very much my way of coping. I would find myself writing, expressing myself and then attending my counselling session. They very much worked in tandem and I was privileged they came along together. It seemed that if there were any pieces of my MS jigsaw missing, I had found them. My spirit was lifted enormously through writing. I just loved waking up every morning, itching to switch the laptop on. Notes, papers, books and boxes filled my kitchen and I could not have been more settled and satisfied!

Writing was a way of externalising my thoughts and feelings and that is what I needed to do. The positive effects have been tremendous and I have got to know myself again. I scratched a bit more beneath the surface than I had ever done before. I found a vulnerable me and I let her out. In many ways, I let her go by opening up through my words and that has been the most empowering thing I have ever done. There were many other different layers there too and I have embraced them all. It would have been a betrayal of myself not to. After all, it's still the same me in this body. For so long I didn't want to get to know the new me. I had rejected her without even realising. My actions showed that. I had simply carried on regardless of what my body felt like, trying to be everything I was before Multiple Sclerosis. I just kept on pushing and pushing, despite how I felt and what it did to my body.

Writing changed my journey – and for the better. I enjoyed the process of writing and editing immensely as well as all the positive outcomes from the entire experience. I was starting to find my place in my new life. Nothing will ever top having my super son Elliot, but writing was an honourable second place.

35

Chongsu Lee

'Courage doesn't always roar. Sometimes courage is the little voice at the end of the day that says I'll try again tomorrow.'

(Mary Anne Radmacher)

What I did not expect as a direct result of writing my book was a serious reduction in my mobility. I can honestly say I became nothing short of obsessed with my book. I would sit for hours writing uninterrupted on my laptop. The days became weeks, then months and before I knew it, years! It was not exactly a planned experience, but one that had evolved bit by bit. My workstation moved from being a soft sofa chair with my iPad, to simply Elliot's laptop at the kitchen table. Neither were appropriate for the number of hours I was putting in. It was a bit too late when I came to that realisation, as the physical damage had been done. I had gone from someone active, exercising and eating healthily, to someone who sat awkwardly and typed on a keyboard for six or seven hours a day. I only stopped in between to prepare dinners and Elliot's school materials. Otherwise I delved back into writing at every spare opportunity I got. I stopped exercising ostensibly and my very healthy diet suffered considerably. Anyone who knows me would recognise that, when it comes to taking things too far, there is a pattern throughout my life. I had done it once again!

My body had stiffened up, incredibly so. My shoulder joints, arms and back ached. I felt it creeping up on me, but ignored the warning signs whilst in pursuit of the final product of my book. There was no question of me stopping writing and I was frightened to pause and reflect on what damage had been done. I chose to plough on in blissful denial. That was until one afternoon when I had taken a taxi down to collect Elliot from school. As the taxi pulled up outside the entrance to the school office I could barely get my legs out of the car door. I had to manoeuvre them manually with my hands, which left me more than a little perturbed. Once out the cab, I literally had no idea how I was going to get inside the building. Telling each leg to step one in front of the other was just not working. The mind was willing them, but they wouldn't move. I somehow staggered inside and took Elliot's hand on the way out. I didn't look up. Stress, sweat and a thumping heart all accompanied me. Enough was enough. It was an absolute big enough shock for me to come to the realisation that going the way I was there may well be a book, but I would not be walking around anymore to see it published. It brought me to my senses.

I had been so happy to find myself doing something that lifted my spirits and gave me real aspiration and inspiration again. Writing had completely blocked out so much of my reality that I understood fully why I had carried on that road so long. I was faced now though with a new and worrying reality. But I would not panic. I would act immediately by breaking up my writing times and interspersing them with yoga poses. I would return to some cooking in the kitchen and I would start swimming again without delay. Onwards and upwards once again.

Except I knew from the outset I needed some greater assistance. I had taken it too far and the reduction in my mobility was significant. My refusal to admit what was going on left me desperately looking outwards for help. I knew deep down that dietary and lifestyle changes were not going to be sufficient to make a sizeable impact, in the short term at least. I had left on the back burner for some time the possibility of a new treatment from a Korean physiotherapist, Chongsu Lee. I had come across him some time ago and read all about his new and pioneering spinal treatment for people with Multiple Sclerosis. I had been intrigued by testimonials from the Scottish actress with MS, Alison Peebles, as well as from the author I followed eagerly, Judy Graham. The treatment involves gentle physiotherapy techniques to shift stiffness in the spine. Multiple Sclerosis means a great deal of stiffness and the writing lifestyle I had adopted decidedly compounded whatever problem I already had. With no hesitation, I made an appointment to meet Chongsu and discuss the options available to me. The time was right and I've always acted on my instincts.

He worked from an Edinburgh-based clinic, Point One. My first appointment did not go to plan as I had what could only be described as a 'funny turn' minutes beforehand. I had eaten some brunch in a nearby café, but on exiting it my head began to spin, I was sweating profusely and I felt a desperate need to lie down. It was beyond strange and so after the briefest of introductions with Chongsu I had to retire from the appointment and return home, inconceivably so, to my bed. After investigation, I figured it was a response to the food I ate. I learned that I react negatively to legumes. I always believe things happen for a reason. On that occasion, it was to delay my treatments. They were to have a considerable impact on my fatigue levels in the beginning and I had some important medical attention to pay to Elliot in front of me.

I returned after a couple of weeks, once Elliot was in recovery from his medical procedures. I was even more exhausted and suffering greater restriction with my mobility. Chongsu was instantly very enthusiastic, positive and inspiring. Without a moment's hesitation, I gladly committed myself to having the treatment. I immediately knew this was the next step in my journey. I listened intently to everything Chongsu had to say and left with a huge bag of hope, excitement and belief. Once again, I had found someone special in the world of Multiple Sclerosis. Medical Research Scotland have commissioned and fully funded a four-year PHD into a 'Spinal Approach to Health and Well-being' at Edinburgh Napier University. Having trained both as an engineer and a physiotherapist, Chongsu decided to mechanise the unique manual technique by developing Robo-Physio. He has received part funding to design and manufacture a Robo-Physio device from the Scottish Enterprise Scheme, the Scottish Government's enterprise development agency. Filament PD, a design and engineering company in Glasgow have taken on this mighty task, alongside Chongsu Lee. The possibilities of the new device are endless and enthralling. It is a big, exciting project and it felt nothing short of wonderful to be part of it.

First though, it was straight to manual treatments from Chongsu. I had exercises to do religiously and although there was a financial price tag, it was not unsustainable in the scheme of things. Treatment commenced and I have never looked back. As mentioned, I did suffer from severe fatigue for the first few weeks. I almost had to surrender to the idea of doing just about anything else. Allan and my sister picked up the pieces of daily life that needed to be addressed. I got by, but no more than that. It was not too difficult because I was so excited about having the treatment and hopeful about what results it would bring.

After eight to nine treatments and over a month of doing my exercises rigorously and routinely, I noticed small changes. I was staying downstairs in the evening playing cards and marbles with Elliot and Allan. My legs did not feel anymore that they were filled with lead after some mediocre activity. I went out to the cinema and for pizza independently with Elliot. I was dropped off and picked up, but nonetheless it was a significant step in my little world. I even became brave enough to successfully carry hot tea to my seat in the cinema! A small achievement maybe to the outside world, but in my MS world it was momentous. They were all baby steps, but accumulatively they made me feel good about myself and my ability. It was early days. It was all very simple. No big miracles. But a noticeable and real improvement in my quality of life.

The tenth treatment coincided with our wedding anniversary. We decided we would stay on in Edinburgh for a celebratory overnight. We planned for a very easy-going evening and waited to see how I felt following my afternoon treatment. I had a good, long rest and drank green tea. Afterwards, I felt up to going by taxi to a local restaurant for an early evening meal. On our return, we would normally go straight to our room for what was left of the night. Instead, and much to Allan's surprise, I stopped at the bar and suggested he ordered some wine and snacks. The Rugby World Cup quarter-finals were on and I thought it might be a good idea to stop off and take in the first half at least. Allan's surprise was a pleasant one and he was delighted to oblige!

I think I was equally as surprised as Allan! I talked, laughed and drank prosecco. What was going on indeed? For me the highlight was my ability to walk to the toilet by myself, but much more importantly without the stress and strain that usually accompanied me. It was the first time in a long time I managed to do so comfortably. The improvement in my fatigue was exceptional. I had put that part of my life and socialising to bed. I had accepted long since it was outside my capabilities. Not anymore, thanks to Chongsu Lee. We went up to our hotel room at half time, after ordering a cheese-free pizza from room service! I went to sleep after enjoying an energy and fun-filled anniversary night with Allan. The course of treatments would last until I had at least thirty sessions and then I would evaluate my progress and future treatments. I had a good way to go and almost couldn't sleep with the excitement of what lay ahead. Although the prosecco helped! What had I unlocked after nearly ten years with Multiple Sclerosis? It felt like I had found the missing and possibly even final piece of that MS jigsaw! I was over the moon, over-excited and, as always, over-ambitious.

36

My Own Little Miracle

*'The difference between what we do and what we are capable
of doing would suffice to solve most of the world's problems.'*
(Mahatma Gandhi)

As the weeks unfolded, what happened brought
sheer delight into my life. I had weekly treatments of
physiotherapy with Chongsu to release the stiffness in my
spine. I carried out my exercises daily, without exception,
to aid that work. I refocussed on the other parts of my
MS jigsaw that were already on the go, but had slipped off
my radar a little whilst writing. That included my healthy
diet, supplements, swimming, earthing and mindfulness.
I had a positive lifestyle going on, which had always
helped keep MS under some control. But what developed
was nothing short of my own little miracle.

I found myself able to do more than just one main
activity in a day. It became two, then three, then four
and I think I topped it at five! I began to go out again
in the evening. I managed dinner, a bar and a late-night
stroll (albeit a short one, holding onto an arm!). I would
spend the morning doing domestic chores only to find
I could write in the afternoon and still enjoy a (healthy)

take-away night early evening! I even started to leave for a swim in the evening. What was going on? It felt amazing! To spend years with so many different doors in your life closed and then for them to start opening again was the most wonderful and miraculous feeling you could ever, ever, ever imagine. It is significant too that this was all happening after the effects of living with Multiple Sclerosis for almost ten years.

When Elliot threw the ball over to me and my leg and foot reacted to whack it firmly and precisely, everyone in the room gasped. I said instantly, 'Do that again Elliot.' My foot connected once more and my aim was accurate. That was only to be superseded within a matter of weeks when I found myself able to do the same thing, but without holding onto anything and with my left foot too! That was met with cries of 'That must feel fantastic Mum!' from Elliot. He certainly got that right and I will remember the feeling in my thigh and foot forever! I could stand up straight from a kneeling position without any support. Having spent the last few years clambering around furniture and anything else that could remotely help me move about, that was nothing less than astonishing. My legs were starting to do what I asked them. I should point out that was only some of the time. Nonetheless, parts of my body were beginning to work again. By the end of the first block of twelve treatments I found myself immersed in a world of new experiences. I would not describe my walking as greatly improved, but enough that I could manage the school journeys and interactions with a bit more ease. Sitting downstairs with Elliot and Allan of an evening became something I had a choice in doing. Elliot was mesmerised as it all unfolded. The excitement was out of this world. I could barely contain myself each day waiting for Saturday to come around for my next treatment. We would set off for Edinburgh, full of anticipation. I could think of little else and only imagine what was still in store for me.

Over the many years of having MS, I had been able to move any issues around my bowel dysfunction to a manageable place. I had established routines and ways that meant it did not interfere with my day-to-day life. But from one day to the next my lingering bowel issue noticeably imporved. It seemed too good to be true, but it was a real and positive difference.

I could think of little else than how many of my symptoms were improving and how the treatment was affecting those changes. The world, and I do mean the whole world, needs to know about this. With the ongoing research into the spinal treatment and potential of the Robo-Physio device under development, the worldwide MS community deserve this information and sooner rather than later. When it is your own life that is at the mercy of Multiple Sclerosis there is absolutely no time to spare. I felt a huge responsibility and still do.

It was not all plain sailing. There were still the ups and downs that come from life with MS and life in general. I had days of unexplained fatigue and days where my walking got me down. But those were turning out to be just days and not for prolonged periods. That itself was an enormous and welcome difference. Those days got less and less as the treatments went on. Chongsu had said clearly to me that the treatment was in no way to be thought of as a cure and there was simply no 'silver bullet' with MS. All the improvements were building to give me a better quality of life, but it would still be a life with Multiple Sclerosis. That was not going to change, but it was so exciting to be living life without those lead legs every day and where the difficult periods with increased symptoms were getting less. Every single day that passed I felt more hope than ever before. I noticed, over a period of weeks, that my feet were not so cold. In the middle of winter they would normally be freezing, but not that year. It was one of those situations where I could not explain the unexplainable. All I knew was that after nearly ten years of cold feet, they held some heat and reassuring tingling. There was still the lack of sensation, but they were of a better temperature for the most part. Yes, it was my own little miracle. I had much more energy and strength. That alone transformed my life. As the stress and heavy burden of my symptoms eased, I became brighter, funnier and happier. I had confidently and with pride described myself as resilient and strong over many years. It was decisively refreshing to be able to characterise myself in an upbeat way again. It had been a while.

Chongsu was a wealth of knowledge and optimism. Every week he had something new to bring and I always left the Point One Clinic with my mind turning over and over with new and deep thoughts. Chongsu put it to me that we are all individuals responsible for ourselves in relation to managing stress and life. He encouraged me to do everything in my power to lessen those stressful times. Put simply, he told me that my body stiffens and responds negatively to stress and that in turn leaves poor physical consequences for my movement and already wavering abilities. That was simply the moment when so many of my thoughts, doubts and worries came to their final resting place. I somehow knew from that day on how to live my life better. If I was ever going to get my body to work again, I would have to change. Chongsu said wryly once that what I needed was to live in a stress-free world! With that not being possible I had to act to get the next best thing possible. I had the realisation that all my thoughts and actions are made of my own choice. In my head from that day forward I would draw a circle around every other person in my life. That circle would represent the division between myself and their good self. It would represent the division in our choices and I would start to let go of my involvement and nervous energy that was so often used up needlessly. I am in control of only my decisions and self. I would not include Elliot in that, at his young age, as we are very much on a journey growing together and learning about life and positive, healthy ways to cope. I became more and more comfortable with the fact I minimised as much stress and worry as I possibly could. I would respect every individual's autonomy. It would be a pleasure and a great release to do so.

It was the start of a new and wonderful chapter in my life. I would go on to enjoy life more than I ever had before. I would care and share in a much healthier way and only after I had made sure I was as well as I possibly could be. Over the course of the last ten years with Multiple Sclerosis I had too often put my own needs to the side. I tried to appear 'normal' and do all the things for all the people I did before MS. Enough. I was tired and weary. I simply didn't want to be that person anymore. My wish was to move forward with Multiple Sclerosis, not pretending it didn't exist. That meant some mighty changes for myself and everyone around me. Through my many simply enlightening chats with Chongsu, I could not wait to get started. It was with great relief and freedom I began to let go. It had taken me to reach the point where I got out of the taxi at the school and my legs would simply not work to realise I had to make some powerful changes. I had only ever thought those changes would involve treatment and physical input. I was wrong. I was learning so much from Chongsu and it was opening a very different emotional chapter for me. I was calmer, more in control and learning to look after myself, Elliot and Allan above all else. Stress had to find a new place in my life. Chongsu was a guiding light. I could feel the benefits of the calmness and the changes I was making day by day. It contributed greatly to improving my overall well-being and ability.

The bag of hope I had carried around patiently for nearly ten years was finally filled with that one non-invasive treatment I was looking for. The improvements to date have been individual and small, but together they offer me a brand-new lifestyle. They are very real changes and their effect on ordinary everyday life is both significant and practical. They have convincingly bettered my quality of life. Happiness comes from the inside out and that acknowledgement has changed my perspective on life and Multiple Sclerosis. I can feel amazing and indeed joyous with a very basic lifestyle and ability. Chongsu has lifted that exhaustive battle with MS, helped put it in a manageable place and refocussed my thoughts and feelings on a spiritual journey. I am inexplicably happy, constantly excited and endlessly uplifted. Quite a feat after nearly ten years with Multiple Sclerosis and all the challenges it has put my life and body through. Chongsu Lee is the most amazing piece of my MS jigsaw.

I cannot at this current time imagine ever stopping treatments. Chongsu aims to reduce the frequency over time, which is something I very much see working for me. It would also help substantially with the costs if they were spread over longer periods. I have the anticipation and huge hope that the device will be able to support me over the long term. Whatever happens, my physiotherapy with Chongsu Lee through the Point One Clinic will be the number one priority in my self-help journey from now on.

Hope is everything. Never giving up is the only option. Belief will take you wherever you want to go. But the answers and solutions will not come and find you. You must go and get them. The search can be long, tiring and riddled with disappointments. Reject rejection and keep on going. When you reach your goal, it can be your own little miracle. It happened to me, so it can happen to you. There was no luck involved in my journey. Just commitment, determination and relentless belief.

37

Robo-Physio

'Great things are not accomplished by those who yield to trends and fads and popular opinion.'

(Jack Kerouac)

I calmly and routinely entered the Point One Clinic treatment room one Saturday morning and there on the floor sat the crude version of the Robo-Physio device. It had ten replica 'fingers' to deliver the therapy at that early stage of design, with the final product scheduled to have thirty-six. Chongsu had been talking about the device for a long time and that it was with the design and engineering team, Filament PD. I wasn't anticipating its arrival quite yet, but there it was, ready to be tried and tested by patients. I had only ever imagined what it would look like up until then and so there was a level of fascination in how it worked and presented.

Chongsu immediately asked if I would like to give it a try instead of my weekly manual treatment. He explained that he himself had been the first person to test it along with one other. He would not indicate any results so as not to influence me, but was clear there were no negative outcomes. I eagerly smiled as my shoulders touched my ears, had a big rush of nervous excitement and replied overwhelmingly 'Yes!'

It felt almost surreal as I stood in the small treatment room in Hill Street, Edinburgh about to test what was no doubt a new invention in the world of MS therapies and treatments. I was nervous, but beside myself with hope and belief. I trusted and had enormous faith in Chongsu Lee. My excitement was off the scale! First thing was first. I had to look, listen and learn what to do and how the Robo-Physio device operated. Chongsu and my sister were both there as I connected with the device and positioned my spine so the therapy could commence. My stomach was in knots, but they were good knots with all my hopes and dreams tangled up alongside the hopes and dreams of the MS population, yet to discover the very existence of the device. I felt a dull pushing motion from right to left and then right again on the different sections of my spine. The device carried a very comforting and almost meditative-like sound. I focussed on it throughout the treatment. The movement repeated with ease and no discomfort. As the treatment went on my spine sunk deeper into the device, but I was very much of the thinking that the deeper the pressure to remove the stiffness, the better. There was the option to reduce the pressure, but that was not the option for me. After a forty-minute session it was time to rest, recharge and wait to see the outcomes. I stood up, unsure what to say or do. There was an unsaid expectancy and hope that I would feel different. A quiet dream that what I had just tried and tested could help improve lives.

I had an immediate response in the strength and range of movement in my legs. But unlike myself, I had to be calm, think and reflect as a great deal rested on my results and feedback. It was essential to be accurate and not let my excitement run away with me.

I travelled home a little tired and reflective on what I had just taken part in. From small acorns grow mighty things. Had I just taken a step in the world of new inventions and the world of Multiple Sclerosis? I arranged with Chongsu that I would test the device twice a week for the next few weeks along with a select few others. I attended the clinic drenched in enthusiasm and hope for each appointment. Chongsu waited eagerly and happily on all comments and feedback. He was never nervous, but displayed calmness and a steadfast belief in his device and the theory behind its operation. After each session, I felt better than the one before. My walking was slightly improved after four sessions. I could climb out of the swimming pool wall steps, independently, with strength for the first time in years. I went shopping and walking in Glasgow city centre with Elliot and Gran for over two hours. I walked longer and further by myself before needing that friendly arm to lean on. It was my first time, shopping and walking, since saying goodbye to the pram. Elliot was ecstatic. I was over-excited and spent so much money that day! I said yes to almost everything Elliot asked to buy. We didn't get out ever, with freedom, together anymore. It was one of my favourite days in my life. Elliot has talked about our shopping trip over and over. It was all thanks to the new Robo-Physio invention. It seemed that quiet dream to improve lives may hold some potential.

I could watch a video of myself walking and accept it was me. I could look at the video without panic and enjoy a higher quality of life. My fatigue left me for those short few weeks. I felt well within myself and my ability to perform daily tasks and asks was improved. I was instantaneously happier. The Robo-Physio invention helped in the world of Multiple Sclerosis. Of that I had no doubt.

The before and after walking videos told of an unfolding success story. Not just of me, but of others testing the device. Chongsu Lee had an invention on his hands and the Filament product design team a mighty job on theirs. Bringing a sophisticated and successful device to life was an almighty task, but one they had already shown the capability and ingenuity to do. It was very exciting. No medication and no side effects. It was early days and all the feedback and information would form the next stage of input for the design and development team. I was hopeful Chongsu Lee and his team had invented a therapy tool that could improve the symptoms of MS. I was optimistic. It was not a cure or anything like that, but a decisive support in the long battle with MS.

It's all well and good banding about '#curems', but people with MS want and need a treatment which is available now, without side effects, that can make a difference to their life immediately. A treatment that can fit in with everyday, ordinary lives. It is here, in the form of the Robo-Physio device.

Then came the phone call to say that it was time for the device to return to the engineering team for the next phase of its evolution. An air of calm acceptance came over me as I knew how essential the work was and that it could bring further improvements to my ability and life in the long term. I have, however, never been particularly good at playing the long game! But on this occasion, I had to dig deep for resilience and patience. As the next few weeks unfolded, I was bombarded by unsavoury school issues and family health concerns. My striking progress began to wane. There was no worsening of my ability, just a simple return to how I was before my Robo-Physio therapy. Whether that meant the therapy would need to be continuous in the life of Multiple Sclerosis was yet to be fully determined, but time and more tests would reveal its most effective use. I had only tested it with ten 'fingers' and the final version would have thirty-six. I returned to Chongsu for manual treatments once again and just as before, they helped me sustain my ability and mobility. I was though left without the very real lift and surge that had come with the Robo-Physio device therapy, but I was not without valuable support.

It can be all too easy to forget how well you were progressing with MS symptoms once you have tried another therapy which propels you to function at a higher level. That, indeed, is what happened to me after my four weeks testing the device. I had to remind myself that the manual treatments had served me very well up until that point. I had to continue, whilst awaiting the return of the device. But every minute of every day I dreamt and visualised the possibilities that would come with using the Robo-Physio device regularly. My MS jigsaw had a critical piece.

Every night when I closed my eyes, that was another

night closer to getting back on that device to have the Robo-Physio treatment. I had moments of dejection and frustration when some things presented as difficult and my walking became laborious and challenging. Particularly as life put more stress and pressure on me and I returned to the laptop for final preparations for the publication of my book. But those were only moments and it was merely a waiting game. I have been on my MS journey for a very long time, living with the ups and downs of Multiple Sclerosis. I could hang on that little bit longer.

38

What's Next?

'I seldom think about my limitations, and they never make me sad. Perhaps there is just a touch of yearning at times; but it is vague, like a breeze among flowers.'

(Helen Keller)

My MS journey has been long and winding. It has had so many twists and turns with every new day bringing hope and anticipation. My life with Multiple Sclerosis has been defined by what I have done, the many treatments tried and all the self-help tools I have acquired. My future with MS will follow the exact same path. I am in control of it. That has been my mission from the very first day and still is. I do not know what the rest of life holds for me and that puts me in the same position as every other person reading this. I do know that I will carry on my self-help journey with the same dedication and drive I have had ever since that very first day and my diagnosis. My MS jigsaw has many pieces after ten years, all of which contribute. I am living a healthy lifestyle. I swim at least on a weekly basis, stretch and exercise in some way daily and eat almost no processed foods. I live an active life every day. My diet is extremely healthy and I drink copious amounts of green tea and water. I make sure I have good rest and relaxation time, mainly with Elliot and Allan. All of that means I am in the driving seat of my own journey and I am not waiting to see what happens. I have developed a range of apparatus to use in this journey, none more so than physiotherapy with Chongsu Lee. I look forward to completion of the new Robo-Physio device. It is simply unknown what the possibilities for improvement and progress will be when it becomes available to use regularly. Its success could offer a new lifeline to the worldwide MS population and for that I am so grateful. All in all, I am equipped and ready for the future.

The fear of the unknown, which has lived with me since the very first tingling and numbness in my feet, never goes away. Every day I wake up wondering what is ahead of me. Every time I walk even a few metres I analyse it. Was it slower? Were my movements more rigid? Was my balance poor or really poor? Was there any power in my legs? Did I stumble? Why did I stumble? The list is endless. I compare and contrast all the time, particularly if I return to the same place after a while. That is all centred on the fear of my condition deteriorating. Just writing that sentence down is hugely unsettling for me as it gives it some recognition. I don't have any definitive answers to those questions. From the very beginning, walking has been problematic in some way or other. Different days bring different abilities. Walking has become a lot harder since I took up writing and my lifestyle shifted to less mobile. But I am working hard to change that. It is yet another MS dilemma for me as I love writing and will keep going, despite the challenges. I adapt and adapt and then adapt some more. Improved fatigue most certainly counteracts some of my symptoms. Otherwise they have fluctuated, but at the point of writing I am full of hope that I can manage Multiple Sclerosis as an active person throughout the rest of my life. That will not be without challenge, but I have gathered many resources to assist me through it. An NHS physiotherapist asked a couple of years ago if I had ever considered using a walking stick. The answer was a firm 'no' as it had so many negative connotations for me and I, disappointingly, held fears of how others would view it. It also induced feelings of panic and ultimately losing control. I am fighting so hard not to let that happen. Even allowing it into my thought process would somehow feel like a submission. Although the physiotherapist tried to propose this from a progressive perspective, pointing out that it may enable me to do more, it still left me with feelings of defeat and that I would be accepting that as my future ability. I absolutely do not accept any such thing. She did give me some food for thought though. However, I am not thinking along those lines. I am focussing on what I can do without walking aids and what else can assist me. I don't know what my future path will be. No one does. I think positively about my future and literally visualise an active and mobile one. I push aside my fears, whilst living in the moment and believing I can and will always improve my ability, whatever I am faced with.

Some of the lessons have been extremely hard to learn and accept. None more so than the fact that so many improvements in symptoms have been temporary. That leaves me always wondering and carrying a feeling of uncertainty and insecurity. That is a difficult place to be on a permanent basis.

If I am being open and honest, which is not in itself easy to be, I would say that the worst part of having Multiple Sclerosis for me has been the falls. After the most serious fall I did have a prolonged period of feeling very low and that MS was getting a bit too big in my life. I have since recovered from that period, but I took the decision to live my life differently from then on. I must do my utmost not to have any further falls. I walk slower (as if that were possible) and I am very deliberate with my movements. If I am uncomfortable with the terrain then I will either not walk through it or I will take the arm of whoever I am with, if appropriate. There lies the reason I only go out with those close few family members! I am very careful now with the shoes I wear. I restrict my trips on the stairs, particularly in the evening, to an absolute minimum. If my legs are tired, I will retire upstairs for the rest of that evening.

No matter what has happened in my life I have always been someone who appreciates what I have. I put great value on all the places and encounters I got to experience. I am still that same person and I am very thankful for all the opportunities and especially the people I shared them with. I loved teaching, travelling, partying and the many experiences I was privileged to have. All of that has changed. Life is entirely different now, but that is OK. I have never missed any opportunity throughout my life and that has helped make this new journey acceptable. I have been able to move on with the same spirit, surrounded by great people. We do different things in different ways, but we still do them. A whole new world has opened up for me. Not closed. That is how I see it, feel it and live it. I love swimming, earthing, yoga, writing and meditating to name just a few. Not forgetting motherhood! All post-MS additions to my life.

Allan and I were confronted with many obstacles and battles even before MS arrived and now with everything we have been through, we share a bond and friendship I never imagined possible. I am full of hope and excitement. Every opportunity shared with Allan and Elliot is special and fruitful. It is the fact I always carry hope that keeps me so positive and moving forward. I embrace the highs and times where I feel well and able. In the past I sometimes pondered the statement that you should live every day like it was your last. Now I do just that. I have found ways to manage on the more difficult days. I can cope with the most basic lifestyle when I must. I am very lucky to have the internet and ability to have so much delivered to my doorstep. I have the best of company every day and am privileged to always have support and lots of love. What keeps me going through all of this is, of course, Elliot. In fact, it would be more accurate to say that because of him I am happy no matter what is thrown at me. Every day with Elliot is special and will always be that way. He is the most caring child and a joy to be with.

We have a very happy home. It is full of laughter and we always have something going on. The sound of bedtimes upstairs with Allan and Elliot are my favourite and most treasured. I often close my eyes and let myself hear those sounds. It would be fair to say that they have so much carry on, it verges on riotous at times! They are absolute best friends. I tried to put in place quiet, unwinding bedtimes for Elliot. Dad just wasn't having it and eventually I gave up! When you hear the fun and laughter you think of this as a very happy and positive place to be. Not somewhere subdued or reserved.

I have become a more reflective person and this whole experience has been the most enormous learning curve I never expected to be on. I have been unable to beat the signs and symptoms of MS. I knew I had to accept this albatross around my neck. There was nowhere to hide and no time to feel sorry for myself. Not that it ever crossed my mind to do so. My aim was to be well enough to look after Elliot and enjoy my family life. It still is.

I give it my best shot to deal with MS every day. I have made good strides at times and coped somehow on the other occasions. Overall the word 'can' is used far more than the word 'can't' in my life. I was faced with a new path to walk – and one I had no idea where it would lead me – nearly ten years ago now. I have surpassed my expectations and hopes. That is thanks of course to a great supportive family and having had the best of medical support through Dr Gilhooly. All the complementary treatments helped too. Finding Chongsu Lee has been a defining moment in my journey. There is also my own spirit as a definite survivor and never a victim.

In the latter stages of this ten-year journey with the help of Chongsu Lee, my confidence has noticeably returned. Elliot's version of that is, 'You're less moany!' I am so much better on most days and not continually living through the slog of MS like before. I am undeniably happier and brighter. I quietly and with reservation state that I have had no major relapses on this journey. Not since the early days before diagnosis and despite not taking any neurological disease modifying drugs (DMDs). I take only LDN (low dose naltrexone) and rely on my self-help tools through my MS jigsaw. The heart of which are my diet and exercise. I have never had one day in those ten years in bed or lying down. But I have had good and bad times. Ups and downs. Energy and fatigue. Being able and not so able. I have worked tirelessly from the minute of diagnosis, changing my diet that very day. Despite pushing myself I still operate on a very basic principle. I do a lot: write, exercise, cook, clean, school runs, earth, trips out and whatever else is required. But at the end of every single day I stop and put back into my MS body what I have taken out. I rest, read, meditate, am mindful, eat and drink anti-inflammatory foods and most importantly sleep long and deep as much as I can. The key is to replenish daily and not wait until my body is drained and exhausted. I go swimming and have spa days for rest and recuperation. I humbly thank Allan and Elliot for always supporting and respecting me and my needs. I am grateful for so much in my journey.

I plan to move to a house without stairs as soon as that is a viable option. I would also consider having the CCSVI procedure done again and see what benefits came with it the second time. Unfortunately, I would struggle to finance it again at the current time as well as the fact it is no longer carried out here in Scotland, or elsewhere in the UK. But those are things I will aim for and try to achieve so that they can help me in the next part of my journey.

Allan and I have stuck together, even in our darkest moments, out of love and not loyalty. We have an open future ahead of us and you can be certain we will make it the best one we can. Everyone has the choice to do that. Everyone has the means in there and together 'wecanfindaway'. It is not what happens to you, but how you get up and deal with it. The best thing in my life was undoubtedly having Elliot. The most challenging was my diagnosis of Multiple Sclerosis. Put them together and you could have a powder keg of insurmountable difficulties. Or you could learn the biggest lesson of your life. You must accept change, even if you desperately don't want it. You must become adaptable and learn to celebrate a completely different lifestyle. Don't resist or fight against those changes. That is true resilience. There is always hope. You can make a difference. Never give in.

We only get one shot at this life. This is the one I've been given. It may not be the one I was expecting. I have coped with everything. I have taught myself that you can be happy with a lot less than you ever wanted or expected. I don't ever dream of a life without Multiple Sclerosis. I do dream always of a better life with Multiple Sclerosis. There is no ending to this story. It will go on as long as I do and I hope its legacy beyond that. I feel a great weight lifted now and a new sense of freedom. With that comes the genuine undertaking that it is in my hands to carve out an even better future. Writing down my journey has taken me to a place I had not anticipated going. My commitment to persevere in my life with Multiple Sclerosis is relentless. I have done better than my initial forecast and I have done more than I feared would be possible. You need to take what you've got, no matter what that is, and turn it into the very best you can. I have adapted and evolved and I have learned a lot about who I am. I'm not just that high-heeled party girl in London and Barcelona. She had a place and she had a great time. But she became a mum and that changed her forever. It changed her for the better. It would be easy to say that MS caused all the changes, but that would not be the whole truth. Motherhood has made a huge impact on my life.

I will treasure the sleepless nights, the breastfeeding sagas, the middle-of-the-night ambulance trips, toddler tantrums, homework battles and so much more. Thank you, Elliot, and motherhood. You will always win over anything else and I wait with bated breath for the next instalment. Elliot and Multiple Sclerosis were 'born together'. They have grown together. They have both taken me on the most incredible journey I had not expected. I glanced in fear over what my life would be like after ten years living with Multiple Sclerosis. I tried to hide away from the terror that struck when I couldn't stop those thoughts flitting in and out of my mind. I am getting very close to that day ten years on. I swim, I do yoga, I cook homemade organic meals (every day), I clean (some days), I play in goal with Elliot, I laugh, I go out (in the car), I drink prosecco, I organise birthdays and Christmas. I meet with friends, I chair the Parent Council at Elliot's school, I travel to watch Elliot play for the school football team (in the freezing cold). I dance (only in my room), I sing (badly), I go on holiday, I earth and I write every single day that life allows me to. I love being Elliot's mum and I have found a way to love me again. I wobble around an awful lot, but so what? It hasn't stopped me. I rely on taxis and cars as well as the support of a friendly arm to assist my walking. Again, so what? It hasn't stopped me from getting around and getting involved. I have never had a day off in those ten years and I never will. I have no intention of that list stopping there. Chongsu Lee has taken my life with MS to a new level. The future feels bright. Weeks before Elliot's tenth birthday and therefore my ten-year anniversary with MS, Elliot spoke openly and honestly after watching me walk, dance (wobble) and play in our living room. I was managing so much more and enjoying playing games and physical interaction with him. He sat down with me only to say, 'It was so hard Mum when I was born and you got not well. You had all those years wobbling and trying.' I immediately felt humbled that he even understood that much. He went on to say, 'Look what you can do now.' I asked him thoughtfully what he had learned from everything in our journey. He said verbatim, 'That things can change, so never give up.'

The most imperative thing in my long and sometimes treacherous journey is that having Elliot has been magical for me no matter what else happened. And I mean no matter what… Multiple Sclerosis has not beaten me; it will not beat me. I give it minimal respect and respond with more ammunition to defy its path. Elliot has stood side by side with me from the day they were both born, as has Allan. We haven't seen it off, but we have put it in a place where we can get on with a positive, ambitious and rewarding future. I am still Tricia in every way imaginable.

Nothing will dampen my spirits in this life. My avant-garde attitude and lifestyle will prevail no matter what life throws at me. I implore everyone to try to do the same. Never give in or be defeated. Never stop, no matter how slow you need to go or how high you must climb. Keep on going and keep on believing.

wecanfindaway.com x

References

1. www.nhs.uk: NHS Choices, Health news, Low vitamin D levels linked to increased multiple sclerosis risk, 27.08.2015

2. *The Multiple Sclerosis Diet Book*: Chapter 2, p.10, Dr Roy Swank, Bantam Doubleday Dell Publishing Group, Revised Edition,1998

3. www.naturopathiccurrents.com: The Postpartum Period – Incidence and Risk Factors of Autoimmune Diseases, Jessa Landmann, ND, 30.04.2015

4. www.chineseacu.com: Chinese Acupuncture & Natural Therapy Center, Learning more about Qi and TCM

5. www.botanical-medicine.org: The Medicine Garden: A Powerful Tool for Healing, JoAnn Sanchez

6. *The Multiple Sclerosis Diet Book*: Introduction, x, Dr Roy Swank, Bantam Doubleday Dell Publishing Group, Revised Edition, 1998

7. www.keepcalmandcarryon.com/history

8. www.mstrust.org.uk: Understanding MS, Facts and myths about MS

9. www.lowdosenaltrexone.org: What is low dose naltrexone and why is it so important?

10. www.sciencebasedmedicine.org: Overview of Homeopathy

11. www.ccsvi.org: CCSVI Alliance, The Basics, What is CCSVI?

12. www.ctvnews.ca: The Liberation Treatment: A whole new approach to MS, Avis Favaro, Elizabeth St. Philip, 21.11.2009

13. www.sciencebasedmedicine.org: Update on CCSVI and Multiple Sclerosis, Steven Novella, 26.10.2016

14. www.everydayhealth.com: Montel Williams's MS Routine: A juice diet and regular exercise, Mollie Bloudoff-Indelicato

15. *Earthing: The most important health discovery ever?* Clinton Ober, Dr Stephen T. Sinatra M.D., Martin Zucker, Basic Health Publications Inc, 25.04.2010

16. www.mercola.com: Grounding Is a Key Mechanism by Which Your Body Maintains Health, Dr Mercola, 02.08.2014

17. www.earthinginstitute.net: Earthing Basics, FAQs, Are you grounded in water – the ocean, a lake, your swimming pool, your bathtub?

18. www.mindfulnet.org: What is Mindfulness?